Proactive Flying

What Every Pilot Needs To Know About Crew Resource Management

What aviation professionals are saying about Proactive Flying..

"After years of teaching CRM courses, I was looking for a fresh way to present CRM/TEM to young prospective pilots, soon-to-be crewmembers, and, ultimately, someday, Captains. The more **Proactive Flying** *I read, the more I realized what I was missing by not emphasizing the core elements of self-awareness, preparation, and proficiency. Captain Mike Taylor has produced a must-read manual for anyone that wants to build a foundation of professionalism based on these principles."*

Neal Bloomquist, Kansas State CRM Instructor, Retired United Airlines Pilot/Instructor

*"****Proactive Flying*** *stands out as an unparalleled text on Crew Resource Management, offering practical applications for flight crew cockpit communications, aeronautical decision making, leadership, and situational awareness. Written in clear and accessible language, the book reflects Captain Taylor's passion for aviation safety and shares invaluable insights from his years of leadership experience. Having used Captain Taylor's excellent textbook as a guideline for teaching several college-level CRM courses, I have witnessed its effectiveness in providing my students with a solid foundation of skills necessary for a successful aviation career."*

Sheri Marshall MAS/ATP/CFII, Aviation Education Faculty, South Dakota State University

*"Captain Taylor's **Proactive Flying** ushers in the next generation of CRM. The fundamental mindsets addressed in this book facilitate the continued level of professionalism that is expected in the aviation community and deserved by the flying public. As educators of aviation, we are intrinsically tasked with the responsibility to elevate the qualitative nature of the aviators that we produce. Doing so consequently elevates the industry's future flight crewmember professionalism. Adopting this book and making it the backbone of my CRM course has been categorically accepted by the students and I very quickly witnessed an elevated level of self-situation awareness within my students throughout the entirety of the read and the newly formatted course."*

Timothy J. Compton, Assistant Director of Aviation Sciences, Baylor Institute for Air Sciences

Table of Contents

Crew Situational Awareness

Decision-Making

Introduction

This book is written for pilots who are in the early and formative stages of their aviation careers. While your initial training will focus primarily on the stick and rudder aspects of flying, your preparation for becoming a competent aviator will be incomplete if it fails to equip you with the skills necessary to operate as part of a crew, and one day command one. The technical abilities that make you a good pilot must be combined with the personal and interpersonal skills that will make this possible. *Proactive Flying* is a manual for developing the traits and qualities that will enable you to make the transition from pilot to crew member to captain.

For current captains, this book will reinforce the crew and leadership skills that have enabled you to advance to the left seat and encourage you to mentor the next generation of pilots who will one day occupy your seat position. While those who are currently captains are already well versed in the value of the principles outlined in this book, there is always something new that can be added to your knowledge and application. I am convinced that the best leaders are those who remain teachable throughout their careers. Conversely, I am also persuaded that those whose years of experience and success have allowed them to believe that they have it all figured out are operating with a command gyro that is in serious need of recalibration.

For those who have not yet made the move to the left seat, I encourage you to actively embrace an identity as a captain-in-training who is preparing for the day when you will be vested with authority to command. Life looks much different from the left seat, and the things for which you now have a simple and ready answer when the ultimate responsibility is on someone else's shoulders may not be so easily reconciled when you are the one feeling the weight of the extra stripe. As a captain-in-training, I encourage you to read the principles presented in this book, consider their application to your present circumstances, and give thought to how you may employ them when you are a captain. The traits and behaviors you develop during your transition from pilot to crew member will define your leadership style as a captain. For that reason it is important that you embrace the principles of *Proactive Flying* early in your career. The traits and skills outlined in this book will provide a solid foundation upon which to build a career as a professional aviator.

Proactive Flying emphasizes the importance of knowledge, skill, attitude, and motivation as essential components of what is required to become a professional. Given that the traits and skills necessary to achieve this goal begin with self-awareness, this book will challenge you to know what motivates you as a prerequisite to understanding how to motivate and inspire others.

While technical proficiency is demonstrated and assessed in the context of your stick and rudder skills, knowledge, attitude, and motivation are components of your *Preflight Self-Check* that must also be evaluated and managed on an ongoing basis. In fact, this book will encourage you to do just that. It is not an overstatement to say that your effectiveness as a flight crew member is determined by the influence of these three components and the degree to which you are proactive in ensuring that they are properly managed.

Your *Preflight Self-Check* refers to a personal commitment to bringing your best to every flight. Showing up for a flight unmotivated or unprepared is a dereliction of your responsibilities to those with whom you are flying and to the safety of the operation. The philosophy behind your *Preflight Self-Check* is that the standards you apply to yourself will determine the value of the contribution you will make to the operation. To the extent that you embrace this proactive mindset, your ability to contribute to the crew's effectiveness will be enhanced.

The skills associated with the roles of pilot, crew member, and captain must be developed and applied with equal degrees of investment. A lack of competence in one cannot be overcome by excellence in the other. Flying is not a profession in which you can get away with simply being good at some parts of the job while excluding others. Being a competent pilot is only part of the equation for success in aviation, and it is the goal of this book to help you develop the nontechnical traits and skills that will equip you to realize your full potential. Furthermore, knowing how to operate effectively as a member of the crew is a critical part of your training to become a captain. The principles outlined in this book will prepare you for the day when you assume the responsibility of being the pilot in command (PIC). Consider this to be a working guidebook on your pathway to the left seat.

Although this book is classified under the broad heading of CRM, the way I have chosen to approach the subject is somewhat different from that pursued by convention and tradition. *Proactive Flying* is built on the philosophy that the established *interpersonal* skills of CRM are most effective when each aviator posses the *personal* traits outlined by the *Preflight Self-Check*. The effectiveness of a crew is established on the competence and motivation of its individual members. The core elements of the *Preflight Self-Check*, self-awareness, preparation, and proficiency must be the foundation of each pilot's personal Standard Operating Procedures (SOP).

Each chapter features a discussion of a particular quality that outlines what crew members and captains "look like," and how they operate. To the extent the *personal* traits discussed in the initial chapters are descriptive of your character, you are more likely to excel in applying the *interpersonal* skills of CRM. Additionally, when the principles of *Proactive Flying* become descriptive of who you are your exercise of PIC authority is more likely to be characterized by wisdom and sound judgment. Flight deck leadership that is exercised in this manner enhances flight safety and also the performance and motivation of the crew. In addition to their obvious application to aviation, the principles outlined in this book have broad application beyond the flight deck. They are useful in any endeavor for which people are joined in the pursuit of common objectives.

Before we address these specific traits, you will notice that the first two chapters are devoted to defining CRM and offering a brief history of its introduction and advancement as a component of flight training and safety. I realize that for many, this is your introduction to the concept of operating as part of a crew. Given this, we will build a solid foundation of understanding what CRM is, why it is important, and how its training and application have evolved over the years.

Let me say word about the frequent use of the word "be" in my discussions of personal and interpersonal CRM skills. Its use in the heading of each chapter is intended to challenge you to embrace these specific traits and behaviors in your personal and professional lives. To the extent you strive to be the kind of person described in these chapters you will develop the operational mindset of a professional. Having an *operational mindset* refers to the attitudes and motivations that define your understanding of what is necessary to operate safely safely and with excellence, and your attitude regarding these goals will define your definition of what it means to be a professional. Aviation is very unforgiving of those who embrace and accept mediocrity and those who are satisfied with low standards are making a choice to undermine flight safety. Such people cannot claim to be called professionals.

> Aviation is very unforgiving of those who accept and allow mediocrity as the standard of performance for themselves or their crew. Mediocrity is abhorred by professionals.

One more thought on what it means to have an operational mindset. The sections of this book that focus on crew and leadership dynamics contain principles that also apply to those times when you are flying solo. Even when there is only a single seat and one set of controls on your aircraft, there are numerous individuals and agencies you must interact with as you execute your flight plan. Working closely and effectively with them is critical to your success.

> You are never truly solo in a moving aircraft, even when you are the only one strapped into a seat. Achieving the goals of safety, legality, and reliability is possible only in the context of a solid working relationship with every agency involved in the operation.

The Non-Negotiables of Flying

In the complex world of aviation, knowledge and skill are the nonnegotiable ingredients for which there is no substitute, and nothing in this book is meant to suggest otherwise. For some, the emphasis on CRM skills may suggest that developing these interpersonal qualities can compensate for deficiencies in the non-negotiables. Let me say with every bit of clarity I can muster that to the extent you lack mastery of the knowledge required to be a pilot or demonstrate an inability to maneuver the aircraft with precision you are not only unqualified for the task, but these deficiencies constitute a threat to safety. No amount of crew or leadership training can compensate for a deficiency in aviation knowledge or skill.

It is also important to note that while many professions make allowance for group identity or affiliation as a template for determining individual qualifications or a metric for defining success, the world of aviation is different. It must be. The laws of physics and aerodynamics make no personal or group distinction in how they are applied and are equally unforgiving to all who violate their precepts. It must also be understood that while it is In the world of aviation the benefits of knowing your job and being able to do it well can be undermined by a lack of interpersonal skills, but it is never the case that the adverse impact of technical incompetence can be offset by a winning personality. You either know how to do your job, or you don't. Charm can't overcome ineptitude, and an aircraft can't be manipulated into doing what you want it to do. Being a knowledgeable and skilled pilot is a prerequisite for becoming a productive member of the crew. The traits and skills we discuss in this book are the icing on the operational cake whose primary ingredients are knowledge and skill.

> The skills of *Proactive Flying* will transform pilots into crew members and equip them to become captains.

Aviation CRM training has evolved since its introduction in the late 1970s and the field has become populated with an abundance of scholarly research that has enhanced flight safety. This book is more an operational guide than a conventional textbook and will provide practical tools that can be applied on a daily basis.

Historically, these skills have been introduced and taught as a supplemental appendix to the technical aspects of flying and have been relegated to a level of lesser importance by many. The traditional approach to flight training has been to train you how to become a pilot and later introduce the elements of what it means to be a crew member. Given that much of your initial flying experience will be solo rather than as part of the crew, this emphasis is understandable. However, it is my contention that being a member of a crew is as much an operational mindset as it is the application of a set of after-market skills that are considered supplemental to the primary task of operating the controls. As I said earlier, even when you are flying by yourself you are never alone in the sense that there are other people and organizations on whom you must rely and with whom you must be able to cooperate effectively to get the job done. As such, the operational mindset necessary for success in aviation is one of understanding the importance of coordinating and communicating effectively with others in demanding operational circumstances.

Before we proceed, take a moment to do an inventory of your own perspectives regarding the pursuit of a career on the flight deck.

Review the following questions and refer back to the final two from time to time as a way of monitoring both the direction of your career pathway and the professional goals to which you aspire. Think of this as a position report. You may be surprised to discover how your priorities and aspirations shift over time.

1. Where/when did you first "test positive" for aviation? Was there a particular moment you knew this was what you wanted to do?

2. Was there someone who inspired you? Who was this person you wanted to be like when you were older? What made you want to emulate them?

3. Where are you currently on your aviation journey? (Experience, ratings, training, etc.)

4. What were your expectations about aviation as you began the journey, and how have they changed with experience? How has this impacted your perspective regarding an aviation career?

5. What are your professional goals? What type of flying do you want to pursue and why? Have your goals changed, and if so, what prompted the shift?

BE MORE THAN A PILOT. BE A CREWMEMBER.

Chapter 1

CRM—What Is It, and Why Is It Important?

Flying Is More than Stick and Rudder Skills

C rew Resource Management (CRM) is a broad term that outlines the specific interpersonal skills whose implementation on the flight deck enhances the safety of the operation and effectiveness of the crew. As stated earlier, the *interpersonal* skills traditionally identified as the core elements of CRM are *leadership, communication, situational awareness (SA), and decision-making.* In addition to these skills, *Proactive Flying* also examines the influence of *personal* attributes such as *self-awareness, preparation,* and *proficiency.* The combination of these *personal* and *interpersonal* traits establishes the framework for the Crew Envelope.

The Crew Envelope

The word *envelope* has a unique application in aviation and is used to define the parameters of an aircraft's design and performance limitations. Pilots are taught to operate within the envelope to maximize safety and operational success and training and experience teach us to appreciate the hazards of operating outside its boundaries. Not unlike the aircraft they fly a crew also has an operating envelope. A crew is comprised of pilots who also have design and performance limitations and, as with an aircraft, safety is compromised when these limits are exceeded.

The pocket of the envelope holds the contents and it is here that the *interpersonal* crew skills reside. An envelope's flap provides security for the pocket's contents and it is here that the *personal* skills are to be found. The *interpersonal* contents of the Crew Envelope's pocket will be most effective when the personal flap is securely in place.

> *Proactive Flying* examines the specific details of the Crew Envelope and the critical role they play in crew effectiveness and flight safety.

The personal and interpersonal traits and skills of the Crew Envelope are interconnected and interdependent. in the matter of your *Preflight Self-Check,* to the extent you lack discipline in areas such as proficiency and fitness for duty you are choosing to operate outside the boundaries of the Crew Envelope. This decision to bring mediocrity to the flight deck is a threat to safety.

The dynamics associated with the *interpersonal* aspects of the Crew Envelope are most effective when the captain exercises leadership with wisdom and discernment. How well or poorly the captain exercises pilot-in-command (PIC) authority influences the crew's ability to work together to enhance flight safety and operational effectiveness. When the captain's leadership is proactive the crew will be more adept at identifying and managing threats to safety. For this reason it can be said that maintaining the integrity of the Crew Envelope depends in large measure on the leadership of the captain.

The Crew Envelope is the model for the CRM skills that will equip you for success as a crew member and one day as a captain. Let's take a closer look at the individual aspects of CRM and their roles in the operation.

CREW: *A Crew* is a high-performance team of pilots who work together to achieve the operational goals of safety, legality and reliability. Each member of the crew must possess the knowledge and skill necessary to operate the aircraft but also the ability maximize team performance through the application of the traits and skills within the Crew Envelope. A crew is most effective when its individual members are equally committed to operating within its boundaries.

A satisfaction with doing just enough to get by with the minimum amount of effort or an inability to consider the impact of your attitude and behavior on the performance of others undermines the safety of the flight. An inability or an unwillingness to consider corrosive effects impact of a toxic leadership style and having a casual approach to individual preparation are excursions beyond the boundaries of the Crew Envelope and no amount of knowledge or skill can repair the damage caused by these deviations. You are an integral part of the crew, and a commitment to excellence in applying your technical skills while engaging with others effectively must be consistent and unwavering. Professionalism requires it, and flight safety demands it.

In order to be an operational asset you must first develop a crew mindset. This involves thinking more in the third person plural and less in the first person singular. Being a member of a crew is a "we and us" endeavor rather one given primarily to the interests of "I or me." As a crew member you are part of the band and not a solo performer.

> You must have a crew mindset in order to be fully equipped to be an operational asset on the flight deck. This mindset begins with the ability to see beyond yourself.

In addition to the interpersonal dynamics of the flight deck, the human component includes the interactions with the myriad of agencies and individuals with whom you engage on every flight. Though we often think of the supporting cast of each flight in terms of their function or role and refer to them as *air traffic control (ATC), maintenance, or dispatch,* they are extended members of your crew whose contribution is critical to operational success. Therefore you must endeavor to understand their role, learn to work closely with them, and be mindful that you share the same operational goals.

RESOURCE: *The Resource* portion of CRM refers to the myriad of tools necessary for a crew to do their jobs. Examples include such things as flight manuals, checklists, and the vast array of technical equipment that comes with the aviation territory.

The abundance of specialized, highly complex equipment available to the crew requires a combination of individual competence and the ability to work collaboratively, and both are essential to operating the aircraft safely and effectively. In addition to being a complex system, aviation is also a dynamic one, and steady advancements in technology result in frequent additions to the volume of information a crew must possess and apply during every mission. Each crew is challenged by the volume of highly detailed operational information which must be frequently accessed, analyzed, and applied in a timely and effective manner. It is impossible for a flight to be conducted safely if critical information is not shared and understood by all involved. Some information, such as aircraft performance limitations, emergency procedures, and certain FAA and company policies and regulations, must be committed to memory. Information that pertains to situations that do not occur regularly, such as aircraft deicing procedures, need not be memorized. However, it is incumbent on the crew to know how to access and apply this information quickly when required and to coordinate effectively with individuals on and off the flight deck. As you can see, the crew and resource aspects of CRM are interdependent. Safety demands that each member of the flight crew and those serving in supporting roles be both skilled communicators and masters of the technical tasks and resources essential for their assigned roles.

> Just as with the flap and the body of the Crew Envelope, the Crew and Resource components of CRM are interdependent.

MANAGEMENT: *Management* is the action word of CRM that speaks to the requirement for the *Crew* to utilize its *Resources* effectively in the pursuit of the operational goals of safety, legality, and reliability.

Given the amount of emphasis I will place on the importance of leadership on the flight deck, the inclusion of the word *Management* as a component of the definition of CRM requires a brief discussion of the difference between the two. Management and leadership are similar in that they share a commitment to the same outcomes, but there are differences between them regarding their execution.

Management is a specific and utilitarian word that refers to the process of utilizing human and technical assets most effectively and efficiently. *Management* is about establishing a playbook for the operation and tasking each person with specific duties and responsibilities. Effective *Management* requires solid leadership. The ability to direct a process in pursuit of an outcome is of limited value if the ability to properly lead those involved is absent.

While *Management* is focused on determining what is necessary to meet organizational goals and prescribing methods for their achievement, leadership is about providing wise and appropriate direction to the team while responding to changing circumstances. *Management* designs the play, and leadership ensures its proper execution.

Leaders consider more than the plan itself and must actively work to balance the organization's goals with the inputs, abilities, and limitations of the team. The best leaders are able to inspire and motivate others to excel at the performance of their duties in the pursuit of a desire outcome.

Leadership must be focused on *doing* the assigned task as outlined by the organization while simultaneously *being* attuned to exercising command authority to provide the proper guidance and motivation for those tasked with the responsibility of its execution. In short, *Management* is about outlining a plan of action, while leadership is about providing operational oversight necessary for its success. In aviation, the focal point of this blended responsibility is the captain. It is not an overstatement to say that the crew's ability to achieve the operational goals of safety, legality, and reliability is greatly influenced by the leadership of the PIC.

> CRM is about managing flight deck resources to enable achievement of the organizational goals of safety, legality, and reliability. In that order. Always.

We will discuss the operational goals of safety, legality, and reliability in greater detail throughout the book and explore their specific relationship to the dynamics of the flight deck, but for now, here is an overview of how they integrate into our definition of CRM.

1. Safety. Safety must always be the primary goal of any flight operations. Without safety, the goals of legality and reliability will be elusive at best. When the organizational emphasis on safety becomes relaxed, this attitude will characterize the operational mindset of its members, and the risk of an accident increases. Safety is as much about the attitude every member of the operation brings to each event as it is about a set of guidelines and procedures that outline best practices for the operation. Data harvested from years of studying the causal factors of aviation accidents underscores the fact that safety is enhanced with crews operate within the boundaries of the Crew Envelope. On this matter, there is no argument.

2. Legality. Conducting operations in accordance with established rules and regulations is the expectation of the FAA, your company, and every individual on and off the flight deck with whom you engage. This commitment establishes a solid framework of order and predictability that serves the interests and welfare of all. Things work more smoothly, and safety is enhanced when everyone involved is equally conversant and compliant with established guidelines. The choice to violate established regulations is also a decision to undermine flight safety and crew effectiveness. Willful noncompliance with prescribed operational guidelines is not only a violation of rules, but it is also a breach of trust that will quickly erode confidence on the flight deck. Captains who engage in or allow such conduct violate the trust of their company and the respect of their crew.

3. Reliability. Reliability has to do with meeting the expectations of others. No matter what type of flying you are engaged in, there are organizational expectations that are clearly defined and understood. On an individual basis, each member of the flight crew expects that those with whom they are flying know their job, demonstrate the ability to do it well, and are committed to operating in accordance with SOP. Your employer expects you to operate their aircraft in a manner that is safe and in accordance with established guidelines. In addition to your employer's expectations, there are also those of the customer. Passengers and freight shippers expect you to deliver them or their goods safely in accordance with what has been promised. In the competitive arena of aviation, those who cannot be counted on to meet expectations will eventually cease to exist. History tells us that more successful organizations will absorb those who struggle to compete, and others will become footnotes of history. The complexities and demands of the aviation system are such that meeting these expectations depends on the interaction and coordination among the various parties who must work together.

Goals are essential for organizations and individuals alike. Having a goal establishes a roadmap that defines your destination and prompts the creation of a plan for how to get there. Goals are important for both personal and professional development, and those who establish goals position themselves for success, while those who have none relegate themselves to a passive existence of simply responding to what comes their way. Not having goals is like having a flight plan with no destination. Imagine taking off with no plan for where you are going and no idea of how much fuel you will need. As foolish as that sounds on a professional basis, to the extent that you lack specific goals for your life you sacrifice the opportunity for direction and achievement while passively accepting life's headwinds. Make it your personal goal to operate within the Crew Envelope and begin this quest with a commitment to personal excellence.

> Not having personal goals is like having a flight plan with no destination. If you aim at nothing, that's what you are more likely to achieve.

Goals also provide an objective standard by which outcomes can be measured. The success or failure of any endeavor can be defined by its degree of compliance with—or deviation from—stated goals. If you aim at nothing, you will hit it every time. In aviation, the goals of safety, legality, and reliability establish clear objectives for each organization and every flight crew. These goals must be embraced equally by both parties and ranked in this particular order—always and without exception. Any organization or crew that seeks to reorient the order of these goals creates an operating culture in which safety is compromised.

When setting personal goals, make sure you are realistic in the targets you establish for yourself and how that relates to others. To the extent that achieving a goal depends on other people performing in a certain way and/or ensuring that specific events happen according to your expectations, your goals are, in reality, little more than desires. Personal goals are achievements for which you alone have the ability to define success, and any goal that relies on the expectation of other people behaving in a particular way is certain to bring frustration. This is an important point to remember because the attitudes and beliefs you develop as a crew member are those you will exhibit as a Captain. Attempting to manipulate the behavior of others in the pursuit of a particular goal is self-serving and plants the seeds for the exercise of passive leadership.

> Know the difference between a goal and a desire, and plan your steps accordingly.

Why Is CRM Important?

According to Dr. Robert Helmreich, *"CRM skills provide a primary line of defense against the threats to safety that abound in the aviation system, and against human error and its consequences."*[1]

Dr. Helmreich was a pioneer in aviation CRM. The industry is indebted to him for the numerous contributions he made to the advancement of CRM and its integration into the operating philosophy of military and civilian organizations. His quote about CRM skills says a lot in a few words and provides an excellent summary of the inextricable link between CRM and safety.

There are two particular components of this quote, *"threats to safety"* and *"primary line of defense,"* worthy of greater exploration as we establish the link between CRM and flight safety.

Threats to Safety

In aviation, a threat to safety is defined as any operational situation, event, or development that increases the potential for human error. Threats to safety increase operational complexity by introducing distractions and increased workload for the crew and require active engagement to mitigate their effects to maintain adequate safety margins. While threats to safety are a reality on every flight, how they are presented to the crew varies with each trip. There are three broad categories of threats that a crew can encounter, and they are either anticipated, unexpected, or latent. Let's briefly discuss each type:

---

[1] "Models of Threat, Error, and CRM in Flight Operations." Robert L. Helmreich, James R. Klinect, & John A. Wilhelm University of Texas Team Research Project The University of Texas at Austin, Department of Psychology Austin, Texas USA.

Anticipated (What you know). These are threats that can be identified in advance of your flight. Examples of these types of threats to safety would include awareness of an inoperative system on your aircraft, knowledge of the requirement to deice your aircraft prior to departure, or a forecast of thunderstorms along your route of flight. These threats can be briefed in detail during the preflight and planning phase of the operation so the crew can proactively develop strategies to mitigate their operational impact.

Unexpected (what you don't yet know). These threats are the unwelcome surprises that show up along the way. Given that these threats present themselves after the aircraft is underway, they significantly raise the stakes. Problems that arise while you are moving through the sky are more difficult to manage than those encountered during preflight planning. This is especially true when they enter the picture during a high workload phase of flight such as departure and arrival. Examples of unexpected threats include enroute systems failures, security threats, or the discovery that the primary runway at your destination has been closed due to an emergency at the field. The presence of an unexpected threat requires a combination of technical and CRM skills to mitigate its effect on flight safety, and these threats cannot be effectively managed by crews who operate outside the boundaries of the Crew Envelope.

Latent (what you don't know that you don't know). This type of threat may not be obvious or even observable to the flight crew but may exercise an active or potential influence on the operation. If you think of threats to safety in terms of how we describe different types of energy, anticipated and unexpected threats are kinetic threats, while latent threats are potential threats. Kinetic threats are active and ongoing, while potential threats are temporarily hidden. An example of a latent threat would be a design flaw in a piece of equipment necessary to facilitate an evacuation of the aircraft. This defect may be unnoticed for an extended period of time—only to be discovered when it fails to operate according to expectations during an emergency. In such an instance, it can be said that the threat was there all along and became evident only when circumstances introduced the conditions required for its activation.

Latent threats exist on both a personal and organizational basis. On an individual basis, cumulative stress resulting from a myriad of life events can impair our ability to perform at the level required for the safe operation of an aircraft or a flight. While pilots are adept at overestimating our ability to compartmentalize the distractions of life with no degradation of our ability to execute assigned duties, the reality is that we are all subject to the limitations that can result from the burden of cumulative stress. To the extent you or a member of your crew carry the weight of the world while putting on a happy face for all to see, you may be shouldering a latent threat to safety that weighs you down and at some point becomes more than you can carry. We will discuss the insidious effects of stress and fatigue in chapter 11, but for now suffice it to say that we are typically not qualified to assess the degree to which such factors threaten our performance and contribution to the operation. The same *"can-do, I can hack it"* mindset that motivates pilots to excel and achieve can also mislead us about our need to throttle back, ask for help, or take ourselves out of the lineup altogether.

> Never let a *"can-do"* attitude fuel a level of enthusiasm that eclipses good judgment.

A latent threat to safety can also develop due to beliefs and attitudes that define an organization's culture. Culture is a blend of the values, attitudes, goals, and behaviors of a group. To the extent cultural norms encourage and endorse practices that are counter to the primary goals of safety, legality, and reliability, they constitute a threat to safety. A latent threat to safety exists in organizations that cut corners on training or attempt to hide systemic problems to preserve a desired image and reputation.

Latent threats are operational land mines, and too often their discovery occurs during an accident investigation.

Threats to Safety		
Anticipated *Known Threats*	**Unexpected** *Surprise Threats*	**Latent** *Hidden Threats*
Inoperative Aircraft System	Inflight Emergency	Hidden Design Flaw
Pre-Departure deicing	Unruly Passenger	Organizational Culture
Enroute Thunderstorms	Closed Runway	Cumulative Stress

Regardless of whether threats are of the right now, around the corner, or hiding in the weeds variety, it is incumbent on crews to be proactive in identifying their presence and developing strategies to mitigate the opportunity for errors. The skills outlined in *Proactive Flying* will equip you to meet these challenges.

CRM skills are essential for managing operational threats to safety and minimizing the errors that their presence invites.

Primary Line of Defense

CRM skills are safety countermeasures that a crew must employ continually. There must be a commitment on the part of each crew member to actively monitor the operation to identify potential threats to safety and coordinate and execute strategies to minimize their adverse impact on the flight.

Lest the neat arrangement of the threats to safety chart suggests that threats to safety present themselves in an orderly and sequential manner, let me be clear that this is not the operational reality you will encounter. Threats to safety often present themselves randomly and unpredictably, sometimes appearing one at a time and other times appearing simultaneously. You can't always predict the type, order, or number of threats with which you must contend, but what you *can* know is that operation within the Crew Envelope is your best defense against the operational misfortune their presence invites. Defense not only wins games; it also enhances flight safety. Fly defensively.

Crew SA and sound decision-making are the safety dividends of a solid investment in your personal preflight, proactive leadership, and clear communication. Bigger dividends are realized by those who invest well.

The History and Evolution of CRM

From Cockpits to Crews

CRM was incorporated into aviation training in the 1970s and 1980s in the aftermath of a series of accidents in which subsequent investigations revealed a significant trend regarding causal factors. In most accidents, it was determined that the weak link in the chain of events that led to the mishap was more often the result of teamwork deficiencies on the flight deck rather than technical incompetence.

One of the most noteworthy and widely studied accidents was the collision between two B-747s, KLM 4805 and Pan Am 1736, at Tenerife in the Canary Islands. This accident was a seismic event in the industry. The findings of the subsequent investigation pointed to toxic interpersonal dynamics on the KLM flight deck as a major factor that led to a preventable tragedy that resulted in the loss of 583 lives. This accident still holds the distinction of being the deadliest single crash in aviation history and has certainly been one of the most analyzed. The question on the minds of the investigators and the world was how a tragedy of this magnitude could happen, especially given that both aircraft were operated by highly experienced and respected crew members who demonstrated no lapses in technical knowledge and skills.

The accident occurred on March 27, 1977, and resulted when the KLM aircraft attempted to take off while the Pan Am aircraft was still taxiing on the same runway. Among the threats to safety that were present on this particular day were low visibility, language difficulties between ATC and both aircraft, operational uncertainties brought on by significant changes in expectations for each crew, and the turbulent interpersonal dynamics among the KLM crew. Neither crew had begun their day with the expectation of landing in Tenerife but found themselves one of many flights diverted there because of a bomb threat at Las Palmas. A lengthy delay at Tenerife elevated frustrations aboard both aircraft as the number of unknowns in their operational equations exceeded that which could be predicted or anticipated with any certainty. This stressful climate was exacerbated by the overbearing leadership style of the KLM captain, whose focus on getting his passengers to their intended destination as quickly as possible eclipsed all other concerns and inhibited the free and open flow of communication among his crew. This captain was a man of immense prestige and reputation at KLM, and his crew was young and inexperienced by comparison. The captain was also the director of flight training at KLM and was more accustomed to issuing directions to subordinates than seeking or accepting input from them. His picture was featured prominently in the inflight magazine, thereby making him the public face of the airline and increasing his stature. One of the accident investigators characterized the KLM captain as a man who did not take well to being contradicted. Given the captain's public and professional reputation and his autocratic demeanor, it is easy to understand why younger crew members would have been reluctant to fully and openly express their operational concerns as they taxied through the fog.

This was the case as the KLM captain advanced the throttles to commence the takeoff roll from Tenerife. He did so as both the first and second officers had doubts about the position of the Pan Am aircraft and wondered aloud if it was still taxiing on the runway from which they were commencing their takeoff. It was. They were less than effective in expressing their concerns to the captain, who was not interested in hearing anything contrary to what he had determined as the best course of action. The captain had made up his mind about the need to get on their way and was not inclined to hear or consider anything that threatened his decision to proceed. This is called a *plan continuation error*, a decision-making trap that can befall us all. Once we have invested ourselves in a particular course of action in pursuit of a desired outcome, there is tremendous reluctance to consider information that threatens to undermine our commitment to our plan. In such situations we can easily become selectively deaf and blind to evidence contrary to what we want to receive and believe. This was most certainly a factor that contributed to the KLM captain's fatal devotion to his decision to commence his takeoff roll amid uncertainty regarding the position of the Pan Am aircraft. As KLM 4805 began its takeoff roll, the crew's reluctance to express their concerns assertively or persistently blended with the captain's insistence on hearing only that which supported his original to create a recipe for disaster. The final exchanges between the individual members of each crew and with ATC were explored in great detail as investigators sought to understand and explain the causal factors for a tragedy of this magnitude. It was determined that the authoritarian leadership style of the KLM captain had inhibited the effectiveness and willingness of his crew to communicate in a manner that would enhance situational awareness and decision-making.

The post-accident investigation focused a great deal of time and attention on the interpersonal dynamics of the KLM crew, and the conclusions were the catalyst for the introduction of airline CRM training. In the years to follow this practice was implemented by airlines around the world and was ultimately mandated by military and civilian regulatory agencies.

CRM and Flight Deck Leadership

The inclusion of CRM as a component of airline training represented a significant shift in understanding the nature of leadership on the flight deck and its proper application in the pursuit of organizational objectives. This new emphasis challenged many of the fundamental assumptions embraced and reinforced since the inception of the airline industry.

The word *captain* has a rich heritage in military history and is one of many words the aviation industry borrowed from the nautical traditions of the British Navy. As the airline industry transformed the nature of transportation in the 1920s and 1930s, it adopted many of the cultural attitudes of the naval service in its expectations regarding the nature of crew duties and flight deck command. These parallels seemed natural, given that the first airline of prominence featured the "flying boats" of Pan American World Airways. Juan Trippe, founder and CEO of Pan Am, named his aircraft "clippers" to acknowledge the nautical heritage of this new frontier of travel.

Nautical terms became a standard part of aviation terminology, and most have been retained to this day. The walls inside the fuselage became *bulkheads*, floors became *decks*, food was prepared in the *galley*, and the clipper itself was steered and commanded from a *cockpit*.

Pilots aboard a clipper became known as a crew, and the person in authority of the clipper and its crew was called the *captain*. Ranks of other members of a flight crew are also carryovers from nautical hierarchy, and titles became declarations of ranking in the chain of command. A first mate became a *first officer*, a second mate became a *second officer*, and so forth. The uniforms worn by Pan Am flight crew members resembled those worn by naval officers and featured double-breasted coats with gold buttons and stripes on the sleeves that designated their rank. Pan Am pilots were the only ones in the industry whose uniform hat covers were white, and in every way, their appearance and command structure mirrored that of the naval service.

With the adoption of these traditions also came the perspective on the nature of authority and leadership that governed life on the high seas. The airline captain, like his nautical predecessors, was considered to be judge, jury, and executioner aboard his vessel, and, in many cases, those who dared to challenge his absolute rule on the flight deck were labeled defiant and insubordinate. This resulted in the development of a culture of strong top-down leadership characterized by complete submission to the will of the captain. This deference reflected a cultural mindset given to the belief that the captain was always right—even when he was wrong. The captain's authority was absolute, and leadership was exercised to ensure discipline and conformity among the crew.

This was the leadership model embraced by the airline industry for the decades preceding the Tenerife accident, and it provides insight into why the junior members of the KLM crew were hesitant to offer information that might be perceived by the captain as a challenge to his authority. Most likely, their reluctance to assert their doubts about the position of the Pan Am aircraft was fueled by an unwillingness to incur the wrath of a senior captain. Reluctance to verbalize safety and operational concerns for fear of being perceived as disrespectful was a common element of the flight deck culture for many years. The Tenerife accident is one of many instances in which this dynamic figured into the causality of an accident. A common storyline for airline accidents involved either an awareness on the part of a junior crew member of the presence of a threat to safety or the possession of critical information that could have averted disaster. The anticipated cost to crew members of speaking out of turn or without permission, even when the safety of the flight was at risk, was such that far too many elected to keep critical information to themselves and hope for the best. As a result they often went to their graves unnecessarily.

In those days junior crew members were to be seen and not heard, and the responsibility of supporting the captain was understood to be carrying out his wishes. This expectation was of greater importance than adherence to the operational standards prescribed by the organization. At that time, there was little opposition to a captain's insistence on operating according to his personal SOP. It was the primary responsibility of each crew member to figure out how to appease the captain to minimize the opportunity for operational conflict. The template for this exercise of command authority was typically stern and one directional. It was not unusual for a captain to instruct his FO (first officer) not to touch the controls or talk on the radios without permission. This hierarchy of command was strictly observed, and for the most part, junior members of the crew did as they were told and spoke only when invited.

This model of leadership in which the actions or decisions of those in command were not to be challenged may have worked well enough in the days when the British Navy ruled the seas. However, the increased complexities of the aviation system, coupled with the tempo of operations made this template unworkable and counterproductive for aviation. The demands to maintain situational awareness and make sound decisions are much greater at three hundred knots than at ten knots. There was simply too much information for one central figure to adequately monitor and address while simultaneously maneuvering the aircraft with skill and precision. The model of the independent leader with sole responsibility for knowing everything slowly gave way to one that would encourage the free and open exchange of information with the captain being the final authority and decision-maker. The captain's role shifted from authoritarian leader not to be questioned or challenged to one emphasizing the need to exercise command authority wisely and appropriately to maximize flight safety and crew effectiveness. This shift was prompted by lessons learned from accident investigations that suggested the need for adjustments to the leadership model of old.

For many captains, this transition was not a welcome one. As is always the case when long-held cultural attitudes and beliefs are modified, there was resistance to and resentment of this new operational mindset. Over time, as evidence derived from accident investigations cited deficiencies in the interpersonal dynamics of the flight deck as causal factors, attitudes about how the captain should exercise command began to shift toward greater acceptance of what it means to lead a crew. This transition occurred on both an individual and an organizational level as the entire aviation industry underwent a cultural shift.

From Cockpits to Crews

Prior to the Tenerife disaster, the common phrase used to account for aviation accidents was *pilot error*. This was a general term that levied a broad indictment on the entire crew to explain what had happened while gathering little in the way of a specific and detailed understanding of how things had gone wrong among a group of highly trained and experienced professionals. The scope of the carnage at Tenerife shocked the world and prompted an outcry for answers that went beyond affixing a generalized label of blame to the pilots. Not only did this event prompt the introduction of CRM training, but also the process by which accidents are investigated. Accident investigations began to closely examine aspects of the interpersonal dynamics of crew members with the same scrutiny given to technical proficiency and equipment malfunctions. As the methodology expanded, it was determined that the causal factors that had once supported the broad conclusion of "pilot error" were the result of specific interpersonal deficiencies associated with the quality of leadership on the flight deck and its impact on communication, situational awareness, and decision-making. It was clear the Achilles heel of aviation safety was most often to be found within the Crew Envelope. Furthermore, greater attention was also given to the quality of communication between the flight deck and outside agencies, primarily ATC.

In the immediate aftermath of the Tenerife accident, the primary focus of the new discipline of airline CRM training was on the interpersonal skills among the crew members. Specific emphasis was given to the need for captains to exercise authority in more balanced and appropriate ways and the empowerment of junior crew members to verbalize operational concerns. Among the conclusions drawn from the Tenerife accident investigation was that the KLM captain's domineering leadership style inhibited the free and open exchange of critical information on the flight deck. As a result, threats to safety were far less likely to be identified and adequately managed when junior crew members were discouraged from sharing their operational concerns.

The combined emphasis on empowering junior crew members while encouraging captains to be more receptive to the inputs of those under their command represented a major cultural shift. This change was received with skepticism by many junior crew members and a blend of hostility and contempt by a significant number of captains. Many captains viewed this initiative as an ill-advised, feel-good program that would undermine their authority. There was a widespread perception about the creation of a culture in which junior crew members were elevated to the status of "co-captain" and skepticism among junior crew members about the ability to reorient the attitudes and perceptions of many captains with whom they flew. For this reason, their standard response to CRM training was typically summarized by two words - "yeah right."

Given that most of the airline captains of this era were former military pilots, many with combat experience in WWII and Korea who were accustomed to highly stressful operations within the context of very structured and hierarchical organizational environments, their initial opposition to this transition was both understandable and predictable. The pushback from many captains was strong and pervasive, and it took some time to convince these veterans that their authority was not being undermined. It also required no small amount of convincing to make the case for the importance of CRM, but in time this hurdle was cleared. A major obstacle to the successful implementation of CRM was getting buy-in from these captains, and it took some time to convince these veterans that their experience and skill were not being sacrificed on an altar of pop psychology. This barrier was made even more formidable by how the airlines chose to accomplish the goal of having their most senior pilots "test positive" for this new frontier of flight training.

Since nothing was known about this novel approach to flight training, the airlines hired individuals from a profession dedicated to teaching people how to interact effectively in group settings. In essence, the airlines thought it a good idea to hire clinical and industrial psychologists to teach old-school combat-veteran pilots how to get along with one another. Pilots with decades of experience as captains would receive instruction on how to perform their duties from psychologists who had never flown an airplane. What could go wrong?

To the airlines this probably seemed like a reasonable approach, given the scarcity of information about this new topic. Yet it would be an understatement to say that pairing psychologists and grizzled veterans from the WWII and Korean War eras was not a winning combination. I remember well the first CRM class that was taught at my airline. The instructor for this ground-breaking event was a highly regarded industrial psychologist with a PhD who had a stellar reputation and glowing recommendations from other airlines who had sought his advice on how to introduce this new approach to flight training and operations. This individual was very much in demand as the industry scrambled to explore and implement this new frontier of flight training, and there was remarkable consensus that he was the go-to expert who could forge the way ahead. Unfortunately for him, the classroom for his first session at my airline included many senior captains whose backgrounds and experience had imprinted them with a hard edge and a low tolerance for what they perceived to be foolishness. These were people who didn't want to waste time with nonsense, and they were not shy about sharing their opinions on matters that fit that category. They were a salty bunch with no time for or interest in talking about such things as feelings and relationships, especially with a psychologist in a room filled with their peers.

As the story goes, the psychologist had not even finished his introductory remarks when the verbal sparks began to fly. The psychologist's first critical misstep occurred during his introductory remarks when he identified one of his objectives as the desire to help these old-timers to think more "relationally" about how to exercise their pilot-in-command authority. "Be touchy-feely and don't hurt anyone's feelings" was the summary statement given by several of the captains in this initial class. (I've sanitized the actual language).

The good doctor's goose was cooked when he encouraged these captains to think about their interactions with their crews as though they were all sitting together in a hot tub and chatting about how they felt about their roles on the flight deck. That was it. He was done. I don't think he even made it to the third slide of his presentation. A chorus of strong remarks and opinions that can't be printed here was the prelude to a spontaneous mass exodus from the room. The teacher had managed to dismiss the class long before the bell rang, and stood there wondering what had just happened. This might be the closest thing to a mutiny that has occurred among an airline crew force. I wasn't there, but with each telling of the stories of the event, I felt both sorry for the psychologist and certain that the CRM experiment would be a short one.

Timing is everything in life, and this was certainly the case with me, as it was in the aftermath of this event that I was asked to join a fellow group of pilots to embark on the task of teaching CRM skills and principles to our crews. By now the stories about the new "touchy-feely ground school" had circulated through the crew force and our work was cut out for us. Needless to say, developing and presenting material to a less than receptive audience was a challenging and sometimes thankless task. It took a while, but with time and the introduction of data derived from respected sources that underscored the value of CRM, general acceptance of its importance was ultimately achieved.

Before the introduction of CRM training, the aviation culture primarily focused on individual skill and performance. The great majority of pilots had spent their formative years of training and experience in a "right stuff" military culture that emphasized courage characterized by a fundamental belief in their ability to avoid mistakes. While skill and courage are positive and necessary traits for those who operate in demanding and dynamic environments, it became clear that when carried to an extreme, these strengths became weaknesses. Many of us who were military pilots remember being impressed with the belief that our level of skill equipped us with the expectation of perfection. We were told that we were the elite, capable of what mere mortals could only dream. Receiving this constant stream of messaging develops and reinforces a belief in the superiority of your abilities, and you begin to embrace an expectation of infallibility.

The image of the intrepid aviator flying solo, and without assistance from anyone, was the model in which aviation was birthed and was the mold into which many of us were poured during our initial training. Capable, fearless, and impervious to the limitations common to others, we were trained and ready to go whenever needed. Never quit. Never err. Never reveal that you don't have your stuff together. And never disclose that you have doubts about yourself or your ability to accomplish the mission. The bravado mindset that united us all was characterized by the language of certainty in slogans such as, *"No sweat, I got this," "I can hack it,"* and, my personal favorite from the navy: *"It's better to die than to look bad."* Being perceived as lacking in the personal and professional grit we all desperately wanted to possess and display was a far worse fate than death.

The recruitment and selection process for military pilots often imbued them with a strong sense of superiority over the less qualified and endowed. Many embraced this belief in invincibility a bit too strongly, resulting in the widespread belief that the commission of an error or requests for assistance threatened the superhero image they had adopted and embraced. Sadly, because of this cultural attitude, pride frequently eclipsed judgment and more than a few pilots were involved in accidents that resulted from their decision to push themselves beyond what was reasonable and prudent rather than fail to answer the challenge. Pilots who were too sick or too tired to fly did so anyway because they couldn't accept being perceived as someone who "couldn't hack it" by an unforgiving jury of their peers. As a result, many perished rather than risk looking bad, simply because their judgment was clouded by the unacceptable thought of being held in low regard by fellow superheroes. The belief that it was better to die than mess up had elevated the fear of public embarrassment above considerations of safety and good judgment. For many, a commitment to these bold words of swagger led to their undoing.

This cultural mindset facilitated the mistaken belief that mistakes could be eliminated by skill and discipline. For this reason, when mistakes *did* occur, there was a high level of motivation to hide them or project blame for their occurrence elsewhere. The commission of an error threatened the mask of perfection and revealed kinks in the armor of those who believed themselves immune to such things. Individual skill and ability were the metrics by which the quest for perfection was measured, and there was little attention given to the importance of team performance or the recognition of errors *when* they occurred. Failure of any sort was a sign of personal weakness which invited open ridicule and prompted a more aggressive desire to ensure that future transgressions never became public knowledge.

This was the soil into which the seeds of culture change represented by CRM training were planted. Among the many challenges associated with this new direction was redirecting an over-emphasis on individual skill to the importance of collaboration with other crew members in the conduct of flight operations. Initial CRM training was called *Cockpit Resource Management*. It was introduced at a time when the belief was that the presence of two or three technically qualified individuals on the flight deck defined what it meant to be a crew. The priority was for everyone to do their jobs with skill and precision, and scant attention was placed on the intangible aspects of the interpersonal dynamics between the individual cohabitants of the flight deck. The C in CRM was eventually changed from Cockpit to Crew as a testimony to a new focus on the nontechnical crew skills essential to working collaboratively in the pursuit of shared goals. A gradual acceptance of the benefits of a crew-oriented approach to training and evaluation took root in the minds of pilots worldwide.

With time, an abundance of new information regarding the critical role CRM played in flight safety and a corresponding change in the methodology in which it was presented to flight resulted in a steady erosion of resistance to its inclusion in flight operations. Among the key factors that enabled this attitudinal shift was the introduction of data from credible sources like NASA and the NTSB that underscored the direct connection between CRM skills and flight safety. As the cause-and-effect link between effective CRM and flight safety became more evident, the perception of CRM as "group therapy for pilots" slowly gave way to an acknowledgment of its positive contribution to flight operations. It took a while for this acceptance to spread through the ranks, and there were a few old-school captains for whom the new horizons of flight training and operation were a bridge too far.

I taught CRM for a number of years at my airline, and one of the old-school captains who attended the initial CRM class still calls me Captain Touchy-Feely to this day. We're good friends, and when he introduces me as Captain Touchy-Feely, I always ask him if he needs a hug or a time out in his safe space. He quickly responds by with a barrage of colorful adjectives that can only be appreciated by a Marine, and we always have a big laugh about the whole exchange. It's all in fun and has almost become a stand-up routine. I'm not sure how I would respond if he ever greeted me by my real name.

Present-Day CRM
CRM is now fully integrated into flight training and operations. Training and evaluation are mainly driven by real-time data rather than a strict reliance on anecdotal information gathered from post-accident analysis. With the development and implementation of programs such as Flight Operations Quality Assurance (FOQA), and Line Operations Safety Assessments (LOSA), flight departments now have the means to gather and analyze data specific to their organization and enact needed policy or procedural revisions in a proactive rather than reactive manner.

Here is a brief summary of these data-driven assessments that have become integral parts of CRM training throughout the industry.

- **LOSA** (Line Operations Safety Assessments): Trained observers ride on the jump seat of normal line trips and collect de-identified data based on objective and observable criteria. This data is analyzed to highlight trends and events that may signal the presence of unknown or latent threats to safety so that proactive measures can be taken to minimize undesired operational outcomes.

- **ASRS** (Aviation Safety Reporting System): This is a NASA self-reporting system that allows crews to anonymously report incidents without fear of reprisal. The focus here is on collecting data that may be useful in identifying organizational or systems weaknesses and applying remedies in advance of an operational incident.

- **FOQA** (Flight Operations Quality Assurance): Systems on modern-day aircraft allow the collection of critical information that can be captured and analyzed to identify potential safety weaknesses. For example, if FOQA data reveals a higher incidence of unstable approaches at a specific airport, a team can study the issue to identify the source of the problem and develop appropriate operational remedies.

Over the past decades, CRM training has evolved from strictly focusing on the interpersonal dynamics on the flight deck to the use of real-time data and the development of a proactive safety mindset known as *Threat and Error Management* (TEM). TEM will be discussed further in Chapter 11 and for now let's discuss an overview of some initiatives that have been introduced as a result of its introduction.

- **Emphasis on active monitoring.** Some years back, the term *Pilot Not Flying* (PNF) was replaced with *Pilot*

Monitoring (PM). This change was more a shift in mindset rather than one that redefined a particular role on the flight deck. PNF was a counterproductive job description, as it highlighted what was *not* being done. As PNF, your assignment identified an activity in which you were *not* actively engaged. The job title suggested that the role of the PNF was limited in scope and responsibility. For many, the role of being the PNF invited a more relaxed approach to the job since PNF responsibilities were deemed to be secondary to those of the person tasked with the primary duty of flying the aircraft (PF). The replacement of PNF with PM represented the deliberate introduction of job description characterized by a posture of active and ongoing mental engagement in the operation of the aircraft with a specific emphasis on identifying threats to safety, and detecting and correcting errors. The passive posture of flight deck observer suggested by the role of PNF was replaced with the proactive engagement of one committed to maintaining an active threat scan during the entire operation.

- **Training and assessment of individual and crew performance.** Initial and recurrent training now includes the requirement to demonstrate both technical proficiency the ability to work collaboratively as a crew member. Line checks and simulator evaluations include an assessment of crew skills in addition to the demonstrated ability to operate the aircraft according to established guidelines. These evaluations emphasize the crew's effectiveness in identifying threats to safety and developing strategies to mitigate their operational impact.

- **Pilot interviewing.** The pilot interview has been expanded to include a CRM skills assessment. A growing number of airlines are including CRM scenarios as make-or-break components of their screening methodology. In these scenarios, candidates play the role of captain in a flight simulation in which a complex operational problem must be resolved in a limited amount of time. Success in this evaluation requires demonstration of sound technical and operational knowledge as well as competence in exercising sound leadership and judgment as pilot in command. Successful candidates are able to maintain their composure while interacting with their crew to gather the data necessary to make a sound operational decision.

- **Debriefing emphasis.** On an increasing basis, airlines are also encouraging crews to engage in a debrief of their performance after each flight. This is an informal process conducted to learn from mistakes rather than to identify and punish those who committed operational errors. This post-flight crew debrief is an interactive dialogue designed to foster an emphasis on learning, improvement, and mutual accountability. We will discuss the post-flight debrief in more detail in our discussion of mentoring in Chapter 7.

Since its introduction, CRM training has come a long way and has now become an integral part of civilian and military flight operations worldwide. CRM's integration resulted in the emergence of an operational attitude that changed the way pilots view themselves and their roles on the flight deck. Pilots can no longer be content to see themselves solely as operators of a complicated piece of machinery. Instead, pilots have come to identify as members of a crew of professionals who share a commitment to safety and excellence. Commission of an error or a request for help is no longer perceived as an intrinsic shortcoming of the pilot. Errors are inevitable, even for the most skilled and accomplished professional.

What is most important is the cultivation of a flight deck culture that understands and values the critical objective of working together to prevent errors from happening and recognizes the importance of developing strategies to minimize the adverse operational impact of mistakes that do occur. The scope of what it means to be a safe and effective pilot has expanded well beyond the boundaries of the knowledge and skill required to operate and maneuver the aircraft with skill and precision.

BE MORE THAN A PILOT. BE A CREWMEMBER.

Chapter 2

The Crew Wheel

Meet the Spokes. Be a Spokesperson.

What Is a Crew Wheel?

Given that many pilots are visual learners, I have included another image to convey the essential principles of *Proactive Flying*. The is the Crew Wheel, and will be the outline for the remaining chapters of the book. Each spoke on the wheel represents a specific personal or interpersonal quality that is critical for operating within the Crew Envelope. Think of the Crew Wheel as the Crew Envelope in action. The Crew Envelope provides an outline of the elements of CRM and the Crew Wheel talks about how to apply them. Think of the Crew Envelope as an article of clothing you see on a mannequin and the Crew Wheel as the opportunity to wear it.

At the beginning of each chapter you will see the image of the Crew Wheel on which only the spoke for the topic addressed by that chapter is identified. Just as a bicycle wheel has structural integrity and maneuverability because of the contribution of its individual components, the different parts of the Crew Wheel are effective tools for managing threats to safety only when they are utilized by each member of the crew.

The three aspects of the Crew Wheel are the *hub*, the *spokes*, and the *rim*. Let's look at each one in some detail and discuss how their interdependence is evidenced in both the design and function of the wheel.

The hub. This is the nucleus of the wheel and the central point from which the spokes spread out and attach to the rim. Each spoke is anchored to this common point yet provides unique support to its section of the wheel structure. Though each spoke has a particular point of attachment to the rim and a unique role in providing support for the wheel, they all originate at the hub. The hub of the Crew Wheel is prominently identified by the word *Be*, the common denominator of a mindset represented by each of the spokes.

The spokes. The word *Be* is the operative word for the individual spokes of the Crew Wheel, and serves as the action word for each trait. On a bicycle wheel, the role of spokes is to hold the hub in place while transferring weight to the rim. Spokes provide structure and support to the wheel, and their proper alignment and spacing enable the wheel to turn most efficiently. There are eleven spokes on the Crew Wheel and in the following chapters they will be grouped within the framework of personal (self-awareness, preparation, proficiency) and interpersonal (leadership, communication, crew situational awareness and decision-making) CRM skills.

The rim. This is the point of attachment for both the spokes and the tire. The support offered by both the hub and the spokes determines how well or poorly the rim and its tire will be able to maneuver and withstand the hazards and impediments encountered along the way. Just as the rim can withstand the force of a bump when the other components of the wheel are fulfilling their responsibilities, a crew will likewise be more adept at responding to operational challenges when the principles defined by the hub and spokes are applied.

Meet the Spokes

Let's take a brief look at the individual spokes and their contribution to the personal and interpersonal skills that provide the structure and support for the Crew Wheel.

Personal Spokes

Self-Awareness. Preparation. Proficiency.

1. **Be self-aware.** This spoke illustrates a dimension of CRM and leadership traits often overlooked in aviation training. While many endeavor to avoid this topic, I contend that self-awareness is foundational in developing the character and personal insight necessary for success as a crew member and as a captain. Understanding the degree to which your attitude Influences individual and team performance is critical to your ability to be a productive member of the crew. Lack of insight about how your leadership style influences crew cohesion and flight safety will erode your effectiveness as a captain. Self-awareness is the starting point on the Crew Wheel because leadership and CRM skills begin in the mirror.

2. **Be prepared.** The next two spokes refer to the more performance-oriented aspects of your preflight self-check. Preparation refers to the importance of knowing your stuff and being disciplined to show up for each flight

rested and ready to perform to the best of your ability. You must possess the knowledge necessary to perform the job and demonstrate a commitment to being technically, physically, and mentally prepared to fulfill your duties each time you check in for a flight.

3. **Be proficient.** In addition to mastery of required knowledge, you must also display skill in the execution of your duties. This requires demonstrating technical competence in combination with a commitment to pursuing excellence. Knowing your job and taking pride in doing it well are the essential traits that define an aviation professional.

Interpersonal Spokes

Leadership

4. **Be Command Oriented.** Anyone who aspires to a leadership position must have a clear understanding of the difference between authority and leadership. It is possible to have legal authority to command while being ineffective as a leader. It is also equally common to exercise leadership without being vested with authority. Authority is an assigned and designated legal position, while leadership is a blend of science and art that when properly executed manifests wisdom, discernment, tact, and discretion.

5. **Be Crew Oriented.** A critical component of leading effectively is the ability to be socially competent and committed to creating an operational climate that fosters teamwork among those under your command. The interaction that takes place during the first two minutes

sets the tone and defines the expectations for the flight. This spoke examines the nuts and bolts of building and equipping your team for success.

6. **Be Coach Oriented.** Few aspects of leadership are more important than that of mentoring. This involves not only the practice of training others but also a willingness to be coached by someone else. Lest anyone believe that ascendance to the left seat negates the need for further instruction let me quickly dispel that notion. The best captains are those who remain teachable and resist the temptation to assume that they have achieved mastery in all areas of their personal and professional lives. I believe that everyone should be the middle part of what I call a *"mentoring sandwich."* In the hierarchy of aviation there will always be someone above you and someone below you in terms of seniority and experience. A *"mentoring sandwich"* exists when there is someone above you to whom you look for guidance and another below for whom you are providing direction.

Communication

7. **Be Engaging.** Understanding the importance of both verbal and nonverbal communication and their influence on the accuracy of what we transmit and receive is critical to flight safety. Effective communication necessitates creating a shared mental model so that everyone involved in the operation has a common level of understanding regarding the critical information necessary to operate the flight safely.

8. **Be Precise.** This spoke features five specific principles that form the framework for communicating in a manner that reduces the possibility of confusion. Data derived from

accident investigations and sources such as ASRS reports identify the most common communication errors between flight crews and ATC. I refer to these latent threats to safety as *verbal landmines*, as they have the characteristics of often being unseen while also having the potential to inflict significant damage by causing misunderstandings that result in unforced errors. These landmines can hide in our choice of words or the use of phrases that introduce ambiguity or confusion into a conversation. Exchanging complex information and instructions with ATC invites special challenges that must be considered with each transmission. For this reason, it is essential to exercise discipline prior to every message transmission.

9. **Be A Mediator.** One of the preventable operational cancers that can undermine flight safety and crew effectiveness is the presence of unresolved interpersonal conflict. To the extent you and another crew member have unsettled differences, both your ability and your willingness to work together are compromised. Such conditions create a threat to safety on the flight deck. This cannot be allowed to happen. Conflict resolution requires courage to proactively engage in difficult conversations that facilitate problem-solving. This spoke is a CRM emergency procedure of sorts, and the steps outlined should be memory items for every member of the crew.

Situational Awareness

10. **Be Operationally Aware.** Flight safety is enhanced when each crew member has an accurate perception and understanding of what has happened, what is happening now, and what can reasonably be expected to happen in the future. This requires an ongoing commitment to monitor the operational landscape and verbalize concerns

in a timely and effective manner. A key component of this spoke involves learning to recognize the most common warning signs of lost or degraded SA and understanding strategies for mitigating its impact on flight safety. The *SA Warning Lights* that will be discussed in this chapter should be thought of as your brain's early warning system.

Decision Making

11. **Be Decisive.** The ability to make sound operational decisions is the ultimate metric by which the effectiveness of a crew's CRM skills can be measured. The personal and interpersonal skills represented by previous spokes can be considered an operational investment in flight safety, and decision-making is where the return on this investment is realized. The quality of a captain's decisions often reflects the effectiveness of his or her leadership. When command authority creates a climate that fosters the free and open flow of communication, Crew SA is maintained at a level that ensures that the captain has access to all the information required to make the best possible decision.

Become a Spokesperson

Each of the spokes contained on the Crew Wheel represents a personal challenge to personal and professional development and will equip you to operate within the framework of the Crew Envelope. This is an inside-out approach to CRM. While traditional courses of instruction are geared toward identifying what one must **do** to achieve specific outcomes, the emphasis here is on helping you **be** the type of person for whom these best practices are natural extensions of your character. As you progressively become someone whose personal traits and qualities correspond to those defined by these spokes, you rightly become a spokesperson for professionalism and flight safety.

Knowing how and when to apply these tools ultimately is a matter of judgment and discretion on your part. The pathway from pilot to crew member and to captain who exercises PIC authority with wisdom is a trial-and-error process. Along the way you learn the nuances of how and when to apply your spokes to achieve the best possible results. This is the pathway to becoming a *spokesperson*—someone whose character is defined by these specific traits.

Your personal and professional journey will include both successes and failures as you apply the tools outlined by these spokes. Be careful not to sniff your own fumes too deeply during the satisfying moments of triumph, and resist the urge to self-flagellate as you digest the bitterness of your failures. Both are inevitable. Neither is forever. Debrief both and apply the lessons that will make you better.

Given that the spokes of the Crew Wheel are intended to be understood as principles rather than rules, consider this to be a guidebook rather than a recipe book. Recipes offer step-by-step instructions with the expectation of a specific, time-definite outcome. A guidebook, by contrast, provides a road map toward a destination for which there may be detours and unforeseen challenges and during which the travel speed will vary.

Embrace the principles outlined by the spokes of the Crew Wheel and apply them with wisdom and prudence, and you will become a credit to the profession.

YOUR PREFLIGHT SELF-CHECK

Chapter 3

Be Self-Aware

Know Yourself and Know Your Limitations

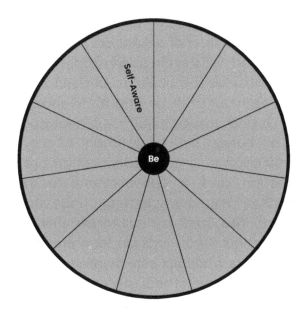

A flight crew is a dynamic and interdependent team of highly trained professionals. Each pilot's knowledge, skills, attitudes, and motivations blend to create an operational climate that influences the crew's ability to operate within the boundaries of the Crew Envelope. While essential for the crew, these traits are absolutely critical for the captain. The personal habits and behaviors that you develop as a crew member are those you will exercise as a captain. If your attitude is negative or your motivation is lacking or misguided during this formative process, your leadership style will likely fail to inspire the trust and respect of those under your command. Such captains threaten the integrity of the Crew Envelope. This chapter begins an examination of the essential items on your *Preflight Self-Check*.

Before delving specifically into the importance of *attitude* and *motivation* as components of your *Preflight Self-Check*, let's take a moment to talk about the importance of self-awareness.

This is one of the most important and least discussed aspects of understanding what is necessary to develop the skills needed to fulfill your role as a member of a flight crew, and is indispensable to understanding your future role as a captain. For our discussion, self-awareness includes the ability to understand the variables that can influence your attitude and motivation, the degree to which your words and actions influence others, and a willingness to engage in an honest self-assessment of areas in which a personal course change is necessary. Self-awareness requires personal reflection and a commitment to inventory your thoughts, actions, and behaviors to better understand the factors that shape them. You can't expect to be effective at leading and motivating others if you lack understanding about how to lead yourself. Leaders who lack self-awareness are ill-equipped to exercise authority over others. An inability or unwillingness to examine yourself makes you less capable of understanding others.

> Crew members who lack self-awareness are ill-prepared to assume the responsibility of command. Captains who lack self-awareness are ill-equipped to lead effectively.

While it is natural for humans to focus attention on individual strengths and personal achievements, professionalism requires attention to areas that need improvement. Regularly engaging in an honest inventory of your strengths and weaknesses will enable you to maximize your contribution to the operation.

On an interpersonal level, a healthy awareness of your capabilities and limitations will translate into a level of credibility that earns the trust of other members of your crew. No one is fooled or impressed by those who pretend to know what they don't know, and no one respects those who play that game. Furthermore, the tempo and complexities of flight operations make such pretending a dangerous practice that puts lives at risk. Faking it—operating behind a veneer of pretending to know everything—is lying to yourself and those with whom you fly. Faking it benefits no one, and those who engage in such dishonesty demonstrate a lack of self-awareness that will jeopardize crew effectiveness and flight safety.

As a captain, self-awareness creates even greater benefits. Acknowledging your limitations and showing yourself to be teachable are behaviors that engender respect among those under your command and demonstrate a healthy attitude that will foster trust and open communication on the flight deck. Captains who exercise their authority in this manner are seen as more credible and approachable, and those under their command will be more predisposed to initiate conversations that address potential threats to safety.

An important aspect of self-awareness is understanding the dynamic nature of life. While particular strengths have propelled you this far in your life and your career, it is important to note that these assets alone do not guarantee continued success. The skills that qualify you to attain a specific position may not be enough to sustain you. I've seen many people who assume that being smart enough to get a job means that they are smart enough to excel at it without the need for further growth or development. For example, scoring high on your ACT or SAT may get you into college, but it won't guarantee success once you are there. The skills required to succeed in college are more comprehensive and complex than those necessary to gain admission. Likewise, the fact that you were the star player on your high school team is no guarantee of success at the next level of competition. Over time you will face new responsibilities and challenges that will force you to adapt and expand the application of the skills that have served you in the past. Those who do so will succeed, while those who rest on the confidence of past achievements as a guarantee of future success risk failure and disappointment. Self-awareness is a critical component of learning how to apply and adapt your strengths while identifying and making adjustments to strategies that are no longer useful or productive. Self-awareness is not a static exercise, but one that must be practiced and honed as you move forward in life. This is true in any endeavor yet is of particular importance in the demanding profession of aviation.

Self-awareness means understanding that what got you there is not what keeps you there. Success requires an ongoing commitment to learning how to adapt to new challenges.

Attitude and Motivation

The most important ingredients in a *Preflight Self-Check* are personal traits that you bring to each flight or training event: *attitude and motivation*. These are critical components of your own preparation that will greatly impact your performance and effectiveness as a crew member. Attitude and motivation affect your ability to contribute to the crew and, by extension, the organization, and will determine whether you will be an operational asset or liability. In the context of our discussion, we will explore the degree to which attitude and motivation influence our expectations, personal discipline, and the development of interpersonal skills.

Attitude

Attitude is a psychological construct that refers to an individual's predisposition or state of mind toward another person, place, thing, or event. Attitude is a complex quality that exerts significant influence over our thoughts and actions and those of the people with whom we associate. Whether at work or in daily life, attitude is learned and evolves throughout our lives as we ascribe value and significance to the people, places, objects, and events we encounter. Attitudes are often developed and reinforced by experience or our upbringing. While attitudes are enduring aspects of human behavior in a general sense, they are subject to change over time.

Attitude is an individual choice and is the one thing over which you alone have complete and total control. While you cannot control your circumstances or the behavior of others, you alone are the final authority regarding how you respond to either. It has been said that the formula for success and happiness in life is focusing 10 percent of your attention on what happens to you and the other 90 percent on the attitude you choose to have about it. There is wisdom in knowing how to discern the difference between what you can and cannot control. Your attitude is up to you, and blaming others because yours is negative is both dishonest and destructive. You are the captain of your attitude. Make it a good one.

Perhaps more than success or failure, wealth or poverty, or individual skill, attitude is one of the most reliable predictors of what kind of life you will have. People with positive attitudes are generally more productive and successful and enjoy greater satisfaction with their jobs and their associations with others. This is not to say that a positive attitude guarantees success and happiness, but that your attitude enables you to apply a healthy perspective to your definitions of success. The positive relationships you are more likely to enjoy with others will follow as an extension of this perspective. Your attitude plays a significant role in the outcomes of life's big endeavors. A positive attitude is a major asset in your quest to become a pilot and indispensable in your ability to operate as a crew member. As a captain, your attitude sets the tone for how you exercise command authority and the type of support you can expect from your crew.

Understanding our attitudes and engaging in an honest assessment of the need to make changes is are key components in making a smooth transition from pilot to crew member to captain. Each of the following statements is followed by questions designed to help you "check your attitude."

1. Your attitude determines your approach to life.

Just as a good landing begins with a good approach, your ability to excel at your job and to work with others in a productive and meaningful way starts with a positive attitude regarding both.

Choosing to make the best of your situations and relationships and looking for the positives rather than dwelling on the disappointments in each forms the foundation of a positive attitude. Many studies confirm that people with positive attitudes tend to be happier and more productive and have better relationships with coworkers than those whose general outlook on life is negative. People with positive attitudes also tend to live healthier lives and manage stress and uncertainty more effectively.

✓ Check Your Attitude:

• **Do I tend to dwell on what is going wrong in life, or am I more inclined to focus on the good things?** Life is hard, and people can be difficult and unreasonable, but there are always good things to focus on and be grateful for. Dwelling primarily on the negative aspects of life and the situations in which you find yourself is the emotional equivalent of spinning your tires in the mud. Everyone around you gets spattered as you spend a lot of energy going nowhere.

• **Is my attitude my own, or am I simply reflecting the values and opinions of others?** Experience and observation have taught me that there is truth in the notion that our associations influence our attitude. We all have a strong desire for the company of people who make us feel accepted, valued, and respected. The need to belong can influence us to surrender our own identity and values and embrace those of the people whose acceptance we desire.

• **Do I spend more time with people who are positive and motivated to achieve, or are my closest relationships characterized more by negativity and a general lack of drive toward worthwhile goals?** Think of the four or five people with whom you interact most frequently and upon whom you rely most. At a basic level, this is your personal "crew envelope." These relationships define your life's envelope and help shape your attitude and motivation.

Humans are wired for relationships, and in our quest to develop a sense of community with others, we seek affiliation with those who share our interests, experiences, or core values. Throughout our lives, we participate in various types of interpersonal relationships and their influence can dramatically shape the short and long-term direction of our lives. Consider these associations to be the crews that shape and direct your life over time. Your continued inclusion and membership in your personal crew requires the adoption of its unwritten code of beliefs and acceptance of its rules of conduct. Your goals become aligned with those of your crew, and their values, beliefs, and attitudes blend with yours. As this relationship evolves and deepens, your character becomes a mosaic of sorts, a blended array of the attitudes and opinions of the other members of your crew. Shared interests and experiences are often the basis for the formulation of a crew, and over the course of life you will experience two different types of affiliations: seasonal crews and life crews. As we discuss these types, think about your current friend group - your primary crew - and give honest consideration to the degree to which your thoughts, attitudes, and motivations are shaped by their influence.

A. Seasonal crews come and go throughout a person's life and commonly function as an extension of shared interests and experiences. The shared experience of going to the same school or a common interest in sports or other activities brings us together with others with whom we can easily relate. Given that our interests and opportunities change as we move to new periods of life, seasonal crews tend to form and dissolve naturally. The things that interest and motivate us at age eighteen aren't the same as those we prefer at thirty, and the bonds of shared experiences tend to shift over time. Because this cycle continues throughout our lives, the influence of a seasonal crew is also more likely to wane with time.

B. Life crews are built on a foundation of shared values and beliefs. These are strong convictions based on what we deem most important, and they establish bonds that are stronger than those based on the transient nature of shared interests. Think of a flower bed. Seasonal crews are like annuals whose ability to flourish is a function of favorable conditions that change with time, while annuals are only enjoyed for a season. Shared values, by comparison, are like perennials. They are more deeply rooted and better suited to withstand the extreme variations that accompany seasonal changes. For this reason, their enjoyment is lasting and ongoing. The value we place on specific things is a powerful and unifying force that determines how we understand and navigate life and is the glue that binds people together in more permanent ways. Life crews connect us to others on a deeper and more meaningful level and have a greater capacity to influence our attitudes and beliefs. Life crews offer a level of acceptance and inclusion that fulfills the human need to belong. These associations with like-minded people provide the added benefit of a sense of validation and empowerment. For these reasons, membership in a life crew is a prized possession for which we are often willing to compromise firmly held personal convictions that are at odds with the attitudes and beliefs of the group.

Memberships often involve dues and, in the case of a life crew, the cost of inclusion is conformity to established norms and customs of the group. With this expectation for greater personal investment as a requirement for membership comes greater opportunity for the group to mold and shape our character. Membership in a life crew is a social contract in which you agree to embrace the values and ideals of the group in exchange for continued acceptance. This social contract empowers your life crew to both influence your attitude and shape your character. Continued inclusion in a life crew requires a greater level of personal investment than a seasonal crew, and for that reason it plays a more significant role in shaping the course of your life.

> We imitate those we emulate, and aspire to be molded in the image of those for whom we have admiration and respect. Choose your crews wisely.

- **Am I in the right crew?** Give some thought to the crew(s) to which you currently belong and ask yourself a couple of questions. "Are the people with whom I spend the most time on a positive trajectory in their own lives?" "Are they people whose character, attitudes, and behavior positively influence me, or do I feel pressure to compromise my standards and values as a condition of continued membership?" "Does my association with these people encourage me to go in positive and productive ways, or am

I enticed to stray in directions that are counterproductive to my personal and professional development?" "Whose approval and validation do I covet most?" Beware the temptation to mirror the values of those who are satisfied with "good enough."

•**How is my attitude being impacted by other influences?** In addition to the direct influences of association that others can have on our attitude, there are other issues to consider. "What online and social media content do I consume, and how much time do I spend in these pursuits?" "How much time and energy do I expend seeking the 'likes' of others, many of whom I have never met?" "How much of my time do I spend comparing my life to the stories others are telling on social media platforms, and to what extent does this practice make me feel inadequate?" "While there are benefits to staying informed and connected to others, it is important to realize that most of the content that appears in online news and on social media sites is negative and in many instances crafted to manipulate your emotions. Overindulgence in negative information adds extra drag to your airframe. A steady diet of negative information will cultivate negative attitudes that hinder your job performance and your ability to work effectively with other flight crew members.

2. *Your attitude is contagious—especially when you are in command.*

For better or worse, attitude is contagious and directly impacts the morale and performance of those with whom you live and work. The attitude you bring to the flight deck will influence not only your performance but that of the entire crew. People with positive attitudes are more likely to appreciate and embrace what is right in the world and are characterized by a sense of hope in what could be. A positive attitude, especially when exhibited by the captain, encourages an operational climate that promotes the free and open exchange of critical information. In these environments, high SA prevails and sound decisions are more likely to result. A positive attitude is very much an essential ingredient to operating within the framework of the Crew Envelope.

For those with positive attitudes, setbacks can disappoint but do not define them or deter their desire to move forward. Positive people don't allow misfortune to sour their overall predisposition toward life or their relationships with others. Positive attitudes hope for good weather at the destination and are able to adapt when the forecast changes for the worse. The new forecast may disappoint them, but they respond by changing their arrival briefing rather than complaining about the incompetence of the meteorology department.

People with negative attitudes tend to have an internal radar that scans for opportunities to be disappointed and unhappy and a microphone with which they make their displeasure known to others. Working with people with negative attitudes fosters a sense of displeasure about both the job and the prospect of engaging with such individuals. A negative attitude inhibits the desire for open communication and detracts from Crew SA and the ability to make sound decisions. Simply put, a negative attitude threatens the integrity of the Crew Envelope.

> A positive attitude strengthens the framework of the Crew Envelope; a negative attitude threatens its integrity.

It is important to understand that attitude and personality are not the same things. People are naturally inclined to be introverted or extroverted, but there is no connection between these personality traits and a person's attitude. Your attitude is an expression of your inner predisposition toward things outside yourself. Your attitude shapes your motivation and affects how others see you and whether or not they want to work with you.

Thus it influences your relationships with others and either draws people toward you or pushes them away. Few people enjoy the experience of working with someone with a negative attitude, and no one wants to work *for* such a person.

If it can be said that a positive attitude is contagious, then a negative one is infectious. A positive attitude fosters enthusiasm and excellence among the crew. On the other hand, an attitude characterized by chronic complaining and negativity is a type of "attitude sickness" that adversely impacts the crew's effectiveness. When I was a junior crew member, the trips I enjoyed the least were those on which I was a captive audience to a captain whose general unhappiness was made manifest in expressions of displeasure with every aspect of the operation and the shortcomings of all involved. The most miserable flight decks are those commanded by a chronic complainer holding court for a captive audience.

✓ Check Your Attitude:

• Am I more given to being upbeat and positive, or is my inclination to focus and dwell on the things that are not as they should be? Are my conversations more focused on what is lacking in my life, or am I more inclined to focus on things for which I am grateful? Am I a chronic complainer? Am I aware of my attitude and how it impacts those around me? Am I a crew member no one wants to fly with? Am I a captain whose attitude makes people not want to follow my lead?

3. *Your attitude at the commencement of a new task will influence the quality of your performance.*

When you are given a task, your mental approach to this assignment has a significant impact on the quality of your work and will determine the level of satisfaction you derive from the experience. Negative attitudes about the job generate thoughts about why you don't want to do it, and your efforts will likely be devoid of the initiative and motivation necessary to pursue excellence. Operational pessimism at the commencement of a flight erodes your level of interest and commitment to performance to the point that "good enough" will do just fine. Don't set yourself and your crew up for failure before you strap in to your seat.

✓ Check Your Attitude:

• Am I given to sabotaging my performance and job satisfaction by embracing a negative or defeatist attitude about the assignment?

> Convincing yourself that you are not up to a particular challenge can become a self-fulfilling prophecy. Don't embrace defeat before the game begins.

4. *Your attitude is a more reliable reflection of who you are than your words.*

Our attitudes reveal themselves in ways that others use to interpret and evaluate the prospect of having to work with us. The nonverbal messages we convey through such means as our posture, tone of voice, and facial expressions can provide a more reliable and accurate measurement of our attitudes than the words we use in our conversations. These are the cues others use to interpret the true essence of what you are communicating. In this regard, your attitude is decoded as a component of what your whole body is telling them. Yes, words have meaning, but nonverbal communication can be more insightful and nonverbal signals are more honest messengers than the words we use. In this context, our attitude cannot be faked and will shape the nature of our relationships with others and our ability to work effectively with them.

✓ Check Your Attitude:

• Am I aware of the nonverbal messages I routinely send to others? Am I displaying attitudes that are counterproductive to developing trust and cooperation with other members of my crew or those under my command? What attitudes and messages do I routinely convey with my posture and body language?

5. Attitude can be your biggest asset or your greatest liability.

One thing that is common to all types of aircraft is the prominent position of the attitude gyro on the instrument panel. This instrument always has a dominant position and is typically larger than other instruments. One of the things you will be taught as you learn to fly is the importance of setting and maintaining the proper attitude for a particular configuration and phase of flight. Every maneuver or procedure depends on establishing and maintaining the proper attitude for the situation. Just as the proper execution of a flight maneuver depends on maintaining a proper aircraft attitude, your ability to contribute to crew effectiveness will depend on your personal attitude.

> In learning to fly, just as in life, maintaining the proper attitude is critical to success. Your effectiveness as a member of a crew or its captain depends in large measure on your attitude.

People are drawn to those with positive attitudes and generally repelled by those with negative ones. This truth should be self-evident. Anyone who has had the experience of teaching others will tell you that they are more naturally inclined to go above and beyond to help students who exhibit a positive attitude than those who do not. You will be amazed at how far your attitude can take you in either direction in life. It can take you forward, or it can set you back. Attitude can be your best friend or your worst self-loathing enemy. The choice is yours to make.

A direct link exists between attitude, motivation, and teachability. A positive attitude fuels the type of optimism that translates into an eagerness to learn coupled with a willingness to be instructed by others. This connection is observable in the example of students assuming personal responsibility for their part in the learning process. Students with positive attitudes take a proactive approach to learning and exhibit behaviors that reflect a desire to excel. These students tend to arrive on time fully prepared for the day's event. Proactive students are an instructor's dream. On the other hand, those who are passive and unprepared make the classroom uninviting for students and teachers alike.

> Ability alone is insufficient for becoming a professional aviator. Proper motivation and a positive attitude greatly enhance your opportunity for success.

Negative attitudes curb a student's motivation and typically create contentment with getting by with minimum effort. People with negative attitudes tend to shift the onus for training to the instructor in the belief that it is his or her job to teach them what they need to know. Such individuals typically fail to recognize how their negative attitudes make them unmotivated and unteachable.

While it is the nature of those who aspire to become instructors to do their best to help their students, there is a natural desire and willingness to go above and beyond the minimum requirements for those students who exhibit a genuine motivation to learn and improve. A student who is punctual and prepared and displays a willingness to do more than the minimum required for the completion of a task generates a reciprocal degree of motivation on the part of the instructor. Over the course of my career I worked as both a simulator and flight instructor. I can personally attest to how the attitude of the student translates into their motivation and teachability and how these variables influence the dynamics of the instructor/student relationship. I'm happy to say that the majority of my students were highly motivated and showed up prepared for their events. Students like this kept me on my toes, and it was not unusual for me to spend as much or more time preparing for our sessions as we spent in the training event itself. These folks were sharp, and I needed to be on my game to give them the best training possible. Working with them was a professional delight, and I enjoyed every aspect of the process. In these instances, my role instinctively expanded beyond instructor to coach and encourager. Students who demonstrated enthusiasm to learn and improve encouraged me to do more to help them succeed, and their positive attitudes became an intangible force that motivated me to take a more active interest in their professional development. I can recall no greater professional satisfaction than watching these students celebrate their successes as they achieved the goals they had set. There is a ring of truth in Ben Franklin's adage that *"the Lord helps those who help themselves,"* and these words certainly apply to the relationship between student and instructor. While it's true that people admire ability, they admire motivation and a positive attitude even more. All are essential for the effort required to transform ability into achievement.

> When a student goes the extra mile to demonstrate motivation and willingness to learn, the instructor will then go two miles to help them achieve success.

This principle applies to every endeavor of life. The attitude you bring to initial flight training will play a significant role in determining success or failure. A positive attitude and the motivation to learn will cause others to be more invested in your success. If you are a motivated student with a positive attitude, your instructor will become your greatest advocate, and those who have been instructors can attest to this truth. In these instances, joy comes from watching your students progress, and their victories are your victories. Likewise, your desire to help those whose attitude and motivation are lacking can easily erode to mere sense of duty and obligation.

It must be said that motivation can be a two-way street. Negative attitudes and poor motivation from those at the top of the organization are corrosive influences that filter down and infect the entire organization to the detriment of job performance and morale. If the boss doesn't care, why should they? It has been said that people don't quit organizations as much as they quit bosses, and my experience tells me that this is an accurate assessment Corruption at the bottom of the organization can be addressed with wise leadership, but corrosive attitudes at the top can be fatal to morale and productivity. When you are in a position to influence others, the attitude you display is the one others will adopt.

✓ Check Your Attitude:

• Is my attitude an asset or a liability in my personal or professional life? Have I considered that there may be a cause-and-effect relationship between my attitude and the level of enthusiasm shown by others toward my progress and development?

6. *Attitude, motivation, and expectations are closely related.*

In advance of any experience, the attitude and motivation we bring to any task are often a by-product of imagining what it will take to complete the assignment. A good deal of the frustration we experience in life results from the chasm between what we expected and the reality of what is happening. Movies, TV, and social media contribute to this phenomenon by cultivating false narratives that foster this disconnect. In the movies, the good guys always win and people live happily ever after. A steady diet of these themes can lead us to expect the same in real life, and when those outcomes don't materialize the frustration that results can easily become the basis for a negative attitude about life. As we invest in the happily-ever-after stories shared by others on social media, a reflective comparison of our own lives can lead us to conclude that we are alone in our struggle to reconcile the gap between expectations and reality and when this happens a sense of pessimism can become a primary component of our identity. No one is immune to this trap, and, as with attitude, the responsibility to reconcile the disconnect is yours. This requires an honest appraisal of your expectations and the degree to which they are realistic. Dreams, fantasies, and other people's experiences are not reliable platforms from which to build your life's expectations.

> Don't build your life and career expectations on the testimonies and experiences of others. Their story is not your story. Write your own.

I remember the first time I sat in my recruiter's office as I began the process of becoming a navy pilot. As he sat there in his white uniform with gold wings and rows of ribbons, I studied the array of pictures and memorabilia from his years of service. They spoke to me about the potential for all of the coolness that I could one day achieve. As we talked, I began to build my own mental model of what life in the navy would be like. I would be flying jets from a carrier deck, visiting foreign countries, and generally looking cool in my uniform as I hung out with my equally cool buddies. Did I mention how cool it would all be? Who wouldn't want to sign up for this? This was the life for me. I took the tests, met the requirements for acceptance into the flight training program, and was selected for Aviation Officer Candidate School in Pensacola, Florida. Off I went with visions of glory dancing around in my naive little mind.

Reality came quickly and dramatically in the form of a US Marine Corps Drill Instructor who greeted me at the front door of the indoctrination barracks on the first minute of the first day of training. When I say he greeted me, don't think for a second that this was an introduction that included handshakes, smiles, and pleasant "nice to meet you" exchanges. Oh no. His face was an inch from mine as he offered colorful assessments about my character, heritage, and general lack of worthiness. It was a motivation speech for the ages, and it was clear that he wasn't the least bit interested in fulfilling my misplaced expectations. This drill instructor seemed to be everywhere all at once, and his desire to "properly motivate" thirty fresh recruits was both relentless and intense. To this day I'm not sure if I was in shock, but I don't think I went to the bathroom for the first three days I was there. This was reality—and it looked nothing like the recruiting posters that had fueled my expectations.

Visions of my potential coolness gave way to sixteen-hour days of demanding training under the very close supervision of tough and seasoned Marines who pushed us beyond what we thought we were capable. Needless to say, this was contrary to my vision of how things would unfold. I remember embracing what I call an incremental approach to understanding and processing the experience. I convinced myself that this immediate situation was simply a speedbump on the road to the moment when the expectations I had brought with me would be realized. In other words, I conditioned myself to believe that this was a brief but necessary hardship that would give way in time to calm seas and blue skies. Once through this tough part, I would tell myself, it would all come together as expected, and life would go smoothly ever after. Or so my reasoning went. This theory of "deferred expectations" turned out to be a moving target that simply refused to stand still. Every level of training and advancement introduced brief bouts of satisfaction that were quickly overshadowed by the introduction of new challenges. There were times when the ultimate goal of getting my wings and flying with a carrier squadron seemed beyond the reach of my abilities.

Without detailing the rest of my navy career, let me just say that I finished training, got my wings, and after a stint as a flight instructor, found myself assigned to a tactical squadron aboard the USS *Dwight D. Eisenhower*. Once again, the expectation I had cultivated about life aboard a carrier turned out to be more a blend of fantasy and delusion than any semblance of reality. Having no prior experience in this arena, I filled in the gaps in my knowledge with idealized notions that could not have been farther detached from real life. It turned out to be nothing like I had convinced myself it was sure to be. Days at sea turned into months at sea and were filled with a wide assortment of mundane and administrative duties and responsibilities that the recruiter had somehow forgotten to mention. Reality was not nearly as much fun as I had imagined it would be. In that moment, I had a choice to make. I could embrace reality and adapt as much as possible, or I could choose to dwell on my disappointment over unmet expectations. I could choose to be unhappy and even blame the recruiter for my frustration, or I could get on with things and move forward.

As it turned out, this became a frequent topic of conversation among my peers. We often joked about our naive expectations as we compared our college-boy fantasies with active-duty realities. Many of us began with the same illusions about what the navy and life at sea would be like and in hindsight were able to laugh about the "teachable moments" that replaced those illusions with real life. However, there were some who were never able to reconcile the fact that reality had not squared with their dreams. They were easy to spot, as they were given to complaining nonstop about everything even though others rarely listened. These people were chronically resentful and unhappy, and their negative attitudes typically translated into poor performance and personal isolation. No one wanted to fly with them, and no one wanted to spend nonflying time with them either. This lesson is important both in aviation and in life, as there will be many occasions when your expectations are crushed on the hard rocks of reality.

More often than not, life unfolds differently than we plan. Over the course of your career, you may be furloughed during an economic downturn or be grounded for an extended period due to a medical condition. Your response to these moments can shape your attitude in ways that will direct the course of your life. You can learn to accept reality and develop strategies to adapt to your circumstances, or you can rail against the unfairness and injustice of life and allow discontent to take root in your heart. The choice is yours. While choosing the former is the healthy option, there is no guarantee of happiness. I can promise, however, that choosing to dwell on the disappointment of unfulfilled expectations will bring misery to you and everyone around you. Be careful not to allow your expectations to cultivate a "vending machine" approach to life, by embracing the belief that a defined amount of effort guarantees a particular outcome.

Real life is complex and unpredictable and can't be reduced to a simple if/then equation. Those who think in these terms are more given to feelings of entitlement as a result of their efforts and will be more prone to they type of disappointment that breeds bitterness.

> Be careful not to embrace a "vending machine" philosophy of life in which you expect the guarantee of certain outcomes as a result of the investment of specific amounts of effort.

In aviation the ability to adapt to unforeseen circumstances is a skill that will be required on every flight. Changing forecasts, revised schedules, reroutes, and unexpected systems anomalies will alter your flight planning and require flexibility and coordination with others to ensure proper execution. Adaptability is key to operational success, and those for whom plans and expectations become absolutes from which there can be no deviation will be limited in their professional effectiveness.

Success in aviation requires that you learn to be a blend of symphony and jazz as you balance what is known and predictable with that which is fluid and adaptable. Symphony offers a very structured presentation of music with a clear plan and from which there can be no deviation. Each measure has a specific number of notes, and each musician must play their part exactly as prescribed. Success happens when each instrument contributes the right note at precisely the right moment. In a symphony there is structure, predictability, and shared expectations among the musicians regarding how the music will be performed. Success occurs only when this methodology is executed as scripted. Deviations from the script can't be allowed or even considered.

Jazz, on the other hand, is a more loosely defined genre and jazz musicians more often improvise and take their cues from one another as they respond to the ebb and flow of a general musical theme. Jazz allows latitude in the inputs of the musicians and what it lacks in structure, it makes up for in theme and individual expression. Whereas symphony is structured and predictable, jazz is fluid and adaptable. When I refer to aviation as a blend of symphony and jazz, I mean that it is characterized by a similar blend of structure and flexibility. Skill at both genres is essential for success in aviation.

> As with many endeavors in life, success in aviation requires the ability to blend symphony and jazz in the pursuit of desired outcomes.

Flight plans, schedules, and standardized procedures are examples of the operational symphony that provides the essential structure of flight operations. Symphony is essential for defining the expectations of all involved, and without it there is chaos. Within the structure of this arrangement there is also the reality that things rarely, if ever, go according to plan. It has been said that no battle plan ever survives the first shot, and this is undoubtedly the case with flight plans. When you walk out to the airplane to conduct the symphony that is your flight plan, you have no way of knowing what factors will introduce the necessity for improv. You have created a structured plan that details the procedures necessary for success, but you cannot anticipate the unknown variables that will insert themselves into your operational equation. A systems anomaly discovered during preflight may prompt a delay or an aircraft swap. Traffic flow may necessitate a specific wheels-up time that delays your push-back from the gate. Thunderstorms may delay your departure or require a deviation along your route of flight, and the weather at your destination may not be as forecasted and prompt a diversion to your alternate. These are but a few examples of the myriad of situations that can require you to engage in varying degrees of operational improv. These elements are examples of the music of operational jazz, and are the surprises that show up uninvited. People whose adherence to symphony is rigid and unwavering can expect to be chronically unhappy and frustrated by the reality of operational jazz. These people usually verbalize their displeasure in ways that can infect the flight deck with operational pessimism. Those with the ability to adapt to unforeseen challenges with a positive attitude while not losing sight of the operational goals will infuse the crew with optimism when they can balance the structure of symphony with the tactical improv of operational jazz.

> Respect the symphony and appreciate its value in providing structure. Embrace the jazz, and understand the importance of improv in the pursuit of operational success.

✓ Check Your Attitude:

• What are my expectations of an aviation career? On what basis do I have these expectations: another person's experiences, movies and social media? How do I respond to the disappointment of unmet expectations? Am I able to adapt as needed when my expectations are not met, or am I likely to dwell on my disappointment? By nature, am I more similar to symphony or jazz in terms of how I approach life? To what degree have my attitude and motivation been negatively influenced by life's disappointments and setbacks?

7. Beware the development of hazardous attitudes!

Having discussed the topic of attitude in a general sense, let's look at the characteristics of those with operational attitudes that adversely impact both flight safety and crew effectiveness.

Allowing or indulging these attitudes on the flight deck indicates tolerance for operating outside the boundaries of the Crew Envelope.

A. The Rebel. *"No one tells me what to do."*

This attitude is characteristic of individuals who intentionally deviate from established operational guidelines as a matter of preference or convenience. People who exhibit these attitudes typically have high opinions of their abilities and are often resentful of having to submit to the authority of those whose knowledge and skills they deem to be inadequate by comparison. Successful flight operations depend on collective adherence to prescribe rules and regulations, which are often summarized by the term *SOP*. More than a simple list of requirements, SOP is the language of operational expectations and Crew SA. SOP is the glue that binds pilots together as crew members and adherence to SOP results in cohesion and operational precision. Each member of the crew knows what to expect of the others, in both normal and emergency situations. Individuals who choose to violate established rules, regulations, procedures, or aircraft limitations display selfish disregard for the safety of the operation and the other members of the crew. There are occasions when circumstances or unexpected operational factors warrant a brief deviation from established guidelines in order to maintain an acceptable margin of safety. However, these occasions are exceptions. Individuals who choose to engage in willful violation of SOP as a matter of convenience or preference betray the trust of their crew and employer and put at risk the lives and careers of all involved.

A common trait among people with this operational affliction is an attitude of superiority. Rebels deem themselves experts with the authority to reinterpret SOP as *Suggested, Optional, or Preferred*. Their disdain for the position of submission in which they find themselves is often verbalized in confident—and usually unsolicited—opinions regarding their own skill and the ineptitude of those in positions of authority. Rebels demonstrate overconfidence in their technical prowess that fosters an unhealthy indifference to risk that often results in poor or ill-advised decisions. Rebels tend to be indifferent to the value of the Crew Envelope.

B. The Dangerously Good. *"Everything will be OK. It always works out."*

Years of success in almost any endeavor can result in the cultivation of an attitude of invincibility and aviation is no exception to this rule. Long periods of operational achievement and successful outcomes can slowly and incrementally allow the development of subconscious expectations of future success. *"The fact that I've been flying for this long and haven't had a serious incident means this will continue to be the case"* is the story we begin to tell ourselves over time. This mindset is characterized by an attitude of indifference to operational risk that will gradually eclipse their judgment judgment in such a way that poor decisions become more likely. Some say that success breeds complacency, and while I believe this to be true, with regard to high-risk occupations and activities, I prefer to use the term *dangerously good* to describe this mindset of the invincible. This term conveys the presence of an advanced level of operational complacency. Warnings and admonitions that were once heeded and respected slowly become relegated to the status of recommendations that the *dangerously good* feel empowered to disregard at their discretion. Operational shortcuts that we once never dreamed of taking become increasingly acceptable, and with time and the absence of adverse consequences, they become our personal SOP.

> Being dangerously good means allowing skill and experience to overshadow judgment regarding risk assessment.

Experience is a powerful and compelling teacher, and there is no substitute for the ways it instructs and guides us. The maturity and skill we develop by performing complex tasks teach us far more than we could ever learn from reading about it or having it demonstrated to us. Almost everyone who has graduated from a programmed course of instruction will tell you that they learned far more from the experience of doing the job for which they had been trained than anything they were taught in class. This is certainly true for aviation.

The seeds of an attitude of invincibility are sewn when we allow years of real-world experience to persuade us to disregard the value of what we learn in class. *"Yeah, that's what the book says, but this works better,"* slowly becomes the mantra of a silent voice that lurks in the back of our minds, and its influence is magnified and reinforced by years of uninterrupted success. This belief can cloud our judgment to the point that at critical times we are tempted to replace what we know with what we believe at the moment as our guiding principle for risk assessment and decision-making. *"Yeah, I know it's not supposed to be done like this, but this way saves time. Besides, I do it this way all the time and never have a problem."*

Ground school presentations that feature analysis of accidents and admonitions to avoid the mistakes of others can become little more than required formalities for the invincible as their years of success has led them to believe that bad things only happen to other people.

To illustrate this point, think back to when you first learned to drive. Before you were given the keys to the car you took a written test to demonstrate your mastery of traffic and safety rules. This was your ground school, and its satisfactory completion was a requirement for securing the privilege of strapping into the driver's seat. As you began your transition from the classroom to the steering wheel, you were very conscientious and compliant in following the SOP of safe driving. You could recite the recommended distances between cars at highway speeds and list all the hazards associated with driving on wet roads. During your initial hours behind the wheel you were vigilant, cautious, and tentative. You adjusted every mirror multiple times before starting the car, used your turn signal to exit the driveway, and were careful not to go anywhere near the speed limit. At this point in your driving career you were more partial to the brake than the gas pedal, and caution was the rule of the day. Every day.

Over time, however, hours of accident-free operation have dramatically altered your attitude toward the potential threats to safety involved in driving a car. As time has passed without accident or incident, caution has given way way to complacency as risk assessment has given way to inattention. The person who once exhibited great caution now gives little thought to the ramifications of driving at high speeds on a wet road while simultaneously performing other tasks such as texting or scrolling through their playlist. It wasn't that long ago that your driving habits were governed by the things you knew to be true, and during your introductory months behind the wheel, you did not dream of driving in the manner that you now consider routine. Months of accident-and incident-free experience led you to believe that the warnings and admonitions of ground school were overstated and this lured you into a willingness to replace what you once knew and accepted with what you believe at the moment as your guideline for risk assessment and decision-making. As your driving record continues accident-and citation-free, this attitude of invincibility will strengthen and you will be more emboldened to be indifferent to the threats to safety associated with operating a vehicle at high speeds in challenging circumstances. The nature of being dangerously good reveals the dark side of experience.

> Experience is a reliable mentor, and successful outcomes are the goal of every flight. Be on guard for the possibility that the combination of experience and success can replace threat awareness with threat indifference.

It is a fundamental truth of life that human behavior is driven more by what we believe at the moment than what we know in principle. In this instance, your driving experience has taught you to believe that you are someone for whom bad outcomes are unlikely, and in that process, a good driver can become a dangerously good one. Consider this the next time you find yourself changing in and out of lanes at 70 MPH on a wet road as you sip your coffee. Understand that embracing the same attitude will be a temptation during your aviation career. To the extent you cultivate such habits in a car, you are likely to develop these behaviors in an airplane. While the type of equipment may differ, your beliefs about the link between experience, success, and safety will be the same.

> The farther away we get from bent metal or doing things that get us into trouble, the deeper our conviction becomes that bad things only happen to other people.

An example of this truth is the common decision-making error of continuing an unstable approach rather than executing a go-around. Experienced pilots are familiar with their organization's SOP regarding the parameters of an unstable approach and the requirement to execute a go-around when these guidelines are exceeded. However, an attitude of invincibility developed and reinforced over time will subtly remind you of past occasions in which you've been able to salvage a bad approach and turn it into a "safe" landing. It can become a challenge of sorts to see if you can once again fix that which is broken, and the fact that you have been cleared to land on the runway that is right in front of you offers the encouragement to press on with the approach. It doesn't seem like that big of a deal in the moment, and though you **know** you should go-around you **believe** you can make it. And why not? You've done things like this before and they have always worked out. Why should it be any different this time? In this moment what you **know** can easily become suppressed in favor of what you **believe**. You'll notice my use of quotation marks as I described the landing as being "safe." To the *dangerously good,* safety gradually becomes a relative term whose meaning is increasingly defined downward to the point that it has a low standard of measurement. When an acceptable landing is defined as one in which the aircraft stayed on the hard surface and nothing was broken, you have become *dangerously good.* You have redefined the meaning of what constitutes a threat to safety. The behaviors and decisions you once considered to be operationally irresponsible have become your own *SOP of the invincible.* As the application of your personal SOP continues without the occurrence of bent metal or unwanted attention from the company or the FAA, it becomes cemented in your mind as operationally valid. For the *dangerously good,* threats to safety and risk assessment become fluid and subjective concepts that rely more on experience and situational convictions than policy and knowledge.

The example of the decision to continue with an unstable approach is especially pertinent given the fact that *Controlled Flight Into Terrain (CFIT)* and *Approach and Landing Accidents (ALA)* are the most common types of mishaps of the dangerously good. These accidents are typically not the result of deficicneices in technical knowledge or skill and in the vast majority of cases are the result of decisions to attempt a landing from an unstable approach rather than executing the go-around. Most of these types of accidents involve experienced crews on routine missions. To the extent the words *experienced* and *routine* are descriptive of your operational routine on a regular basis, be on guard for the warning signs of complacency that point to becoming *dangerously good*.

It is worth repeating that the personal qualities necessary for becoming a productive crew member and one day exercising command begins with a look in the mirror. This requires a healthy degree of self-awareness that includes, but is not limited to, the following principles and guidelines. You will notice that each category is headed by a statement describing something that you must know about yourself, followed by a list of specific recommendations for personal application.

Know Your Strengths and How to Apply Them Effectively

1. **Be mindful that the strengths that got you here may not guarantee long-term success.** Life is not a static process, and adaptability is essential for growth and development.

2. **Be humble about what you are good at.** Embrace the value of blending symphony and jazz in your personal and professional endeavors.

3. **Be mindful of what motivates you.** Endeavor to understand the *why* behind your pursuits and develop realistic goals and expectations.

Know Your Weaknesses and How to Pursue Growth

1. **Be honest about your shortcomings.** Acknowledge your imperfections. Spend more time practicing the things you are not good at than those at which you excel. Refuse to let fear of failure make you indecisive to the point that you are incapable of making tough decisions. Refuse to shy away from challenges that may expose weaknesses. Perhaps your greatest fear will be realized when you discover that you're not as good at something as everyone thinks you are. Recognize and capitalize such teachable moments and use them to recalibrate beliefs and assumptions that frame your self-image.

2. **Be teachable.** Accept guidance and instruction from a trusted mentor. Choose a mentor who is a coach rather than a cheerleader. Debrief after each flight. If you actively avoid performance feedback, ask yourself what is driving this behavior. Our capacity for self-deception can convince us that bad news doesn't exist if we don't hear it. Don't run from constructive criticism.

3. **Be disciplined.** Just as you must scan for threats to safety on the flight deck, develop a scan pattern for the presence of counterproductive attitudes and habits, and change your life vectors as necessary. Choose to associate with people whose influence encourages forward progress in life as opposed to those satisfied with mediocrity.

> Much of life is a leadership academy, and its lessons can't be learned by those who lack motivation to learn and improve.

Know Your Influence

1. **Be attuned to how your words and behavior impact others.** Learn to live beyond yourself. Remember that no one lives in a vacuum, and consider how the things you say and do can influence the beliefs and actions of others.

2. **Be perceptive.** Learn to listen between the lines when others are talking. Become a student of nonverbal communication.

3. **Be consistent.** Don't hold others to a standard to which you are unwilling to comply. Few things erode the trust and respect of those under your command more quickly and thoroughly.

Know Your Boundaries

1. **Be willing to say no.** You don't have to comply with a request simply because someone asked you to. Be helpful when you can, but learn how to discern and avoid the trap of enslavement to the expectations of others. When declining a request, endeavor to inform more and explain less. An explanation offered when none has been requested sounds like an excuse. Don't be afraid to use "no" as a complete sentence.

2. **Be strong enough to be unpopular. Command can be lonely.** Don't allow the affirmation of others to be the primary motivation that governs your decisions. To the extent your decisions are unduly influenced by the expectations and desires of others, you give them command. Don't surrender your stripes.

3. **Be willing to acknowledge your limitations.** Pilots have deep respect that borders on reverence about operating within the design capabilities of their aircraft. No one willingly lowers the gear or extends the flaps at speeds in excess of their operational limitations. When it comes to acknowledging personal limitations, however, we tend to rely on subjective assessments of our performance capabilities. We are far more respectful of the boundaries of the aircraft's envelope than those of the Crew Envelope. Factors such as personal stress and fatigue can diminish performance to the point that we are ill-equipped to perform our duties and responsibilities. Know your personal design limits and demonstrate the wisdom necessary to operate within this framework. Professionals must exercise the discipline necessary to know when they have no business strapping in to an aircraft.

A common denominator in flying and life is the requirement to maintain an accurate degree of awareness regarding your current position and course and compare it with where you need to be. The aviation system is replete with systems and procedures to help with this process, including position reports, altitude alerts, and EGPWS warnings. One of the self-assessment tools upon which you will rely regularly is the *Precision Approach Path Indicator (PAPI)*. The PAPI is a fixture adjacent to a runway that enables the crew to assess their current position on the glide path as compared to where they need to be to facilitate a safe landing. The PAPI is a real-time self-assessment guide that tells you if you are too high, too low, or just right on your approach. Information from the PAPI is used to make the necessary adjustments and the need to monitor and respond to its messaging is ongoing.

Using the theme of the PAPI, I developed the following self-assessment tool for use in determining your present position on your personal and professional glide path as you seek to develop the traits outlined on the Crew Wheel. This personal PAPI is organized into four categories: *Preparation, Attitude, Proficiency, and Interpersonal skills.*

This tool only works for those who are honest with themselves regarding their position and their need for adjustments to their glide path. I caution you to be mindful of the capacity every human has for engaging in self-deception. It is our natural inclination to overestimate our strengths and minimize our weaknesses. We are prone to give ourselves the benefit of the doubt for infractions for which we hold others to a high standard of accountability. For example, when other people lie, it's easy to paint with a broad brush of judgment as we point out their faults. *"He/she is a liar,"* we say. However, when we lie, our immediate impulse is to justify and excuse our behavior, and a typical response will sound something like, *"Well, it's complicated. I can explain."* We all wander from our desired glide path from time to time, and I hope that this personal PAPI will be helpful as you strive to make the adjustments necessary for success.

For this reason, I recommend you seek the input and perspective of someone whose insights you trust as you ponder the specifics of this PAPI. Find a mentor, someone whose knowledge and experience are respected and credible. Most importantly, it is important to select someone who is not afraid to tell you the hard things that you are unlikely to tell yourself. Find a mentor who cares about you enough to tell you what you need to hear. Avoid selecting someone who will simply tell you what you want to hear . . . or that you are awesome. (Especially avoid people who are inclined to tell everyone that they are awesome.) Choosing a mentor who will tell you only happy tales is the easy way, and it has been my experience that in most of the essential matters of life, the easy way is rarely the best way.

Preparation
- Do I know my stuff?
- Do I show up rested and ready for every flight?
- Do I stay current on policies and procedures?

Attitude
- Am I someone who takes initiative?
- Am I content with "good enough?"
- Am I teachable?

Proficiency
- Do I comply with SOP?
- Do I proactively scan for threats to safety?
- Do I know the warning signs of being dangerously good?

Interpersonal Skills
- Am I mindful of my influence over others?
- Am I equally committed to speaking and listening?
- Am I willing to engage with others to resolve conflict?

Given that the goal of every pilot and crew member is to one day be a captain whose command authority is exercised with wisdom and discretion, it is important to understand the role that self-awareness plays in the development of the qualities necessary for this pursuit. Those who fail to give serious thought to understanding what shapes their own attitudes and what motivates their behavior are ill-equipped to lead others. Devote time and attention to an honest inventory of both. Ongoing practice in managing yourself enhances your ability to lead others.

YOUR PREFLIGHT SELF-CHECK

Chapter 4

Be Proficient. Be Prepared

Know Your Stuff and Take Pride in Doing Your Job Well

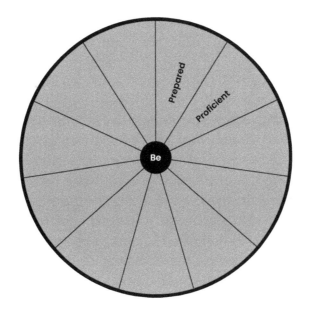

While CRM courses and publications have traditionally focused on the interpersonal nature of CRM and the application of these skills, it is important to understand the critical role that the individual skills of proficiency and preparation play in determining a crew's ability to operate in a safe and effective manner. At a basic level, a crew is only as good as the competence and dedication of each of its members. Deficiencies in individual proficiency and a lack of commitment to the disciplines necessary to be prepared to operate at a high level for each flight are corrosive elements that will undermine the effectiveness of any crew and jeopardize flight safety. Pilots who operate within the boundaries of the Crew Envelope are more likely to pursue excellence in their professional behavior and can be relied upon to do what is necessary to ensure their fitness for duty before each flight. The word *proficiency* refers to maintaining a high level of knowledge and skill. Knowing your job and taking pride in doing it well are essential to success in any endeavor, especially one that requires the ability to operate with precision in a highly dynamic environment in which the consequences of incompetence can be catastrophic. Proficiency and preparation are operational muscles that will atrophy with a lack of exercise.

The spokes of the Crew Wheel underscore both the technical and mental aspects of what is expected by the other members of your crew and what you should expect of yourself. No one lives or operates in a vacuum, and your attention to the personal aspects of proficiency and preparation are demonstrations of accountability to the profession and to those with whom you fly. Every pilot owes it to their fellow crew members to show up for duty fully rested and prepared to operate at the highest level of their ability. Inattention, a poor attitude, and a lack of self-discipline are selfish indulgences that undermine safety and demonstrate a lack of commitment to the profession and the welfare of your fellow crew members.

Proficiency—Knowledge and Skill

Know your stuff and endeavor to do your job with excellence.

A critical component of what's necessary to succeed in any endeavor is individual competence. In aviation, competence is a combination of understanding the complexities of the job and taking pride in its proper execution. In a profession in which people entrust themselves to your care with the belief that you know what you are doing there is no place for those who are not good at their job, or who embrace attitudes that convey a sense of contentment to put forth the minimum amount of effort. Flight decks are work zones for which the margins for error are small and the penalties for incompetence, inattention, or neglect can be fatal. As such, it is incumbent on every pilot to be knowledgeable in all aspects of the job. A commitment to personal proficiency is the starting point for being considered a professional.

Knowledge—Know Your Stuff

Let's examine some of the specifics with regard to knowledge and skill. As with many professions, aviation knowledge is both static and dynamic. There is knowledge that is fixed and that which is revised over time. Let's take a look at each type in some detail.

Static Knowledge

This refers to the unchanging facts that establish the foundation for aviation. The principles of aerodynamics, aircraft performance, and an understanding of the essential rules and regulations that govern the industry are examples of static knowledge. Static knowledge is unwavering and demands strict compliance and adherence to its maxims and decrees, and the penalties for violation can be catastrophic. The principles of aerodynamics and aircraft performance are nonnegotiable aspects of physics for which each crew must be not only conversant but also respectful of the consequences of operating outside their boundaries. The repurcussions of carelessness, neglect, or a failure to operate within these confines imposes penalties that are both serious and certain. Unlike endeavors in which subjective considerations such as your affiliation with a particular group can afford a certain amount of latitude or consideration for violations of established guidelines, aviation operates on a simple principle: you either know your job and how to do it well, or you don't. Those who demonstrate the requisite knowledge and skill are equipped to be successful, while those who don't are a hazard to themselves and others. Airplanes don't care about your background or your social affiliations and punish any and all who violate its fundamental rules with equal fervor.

Aviation is a demanding profession, and the amount of information that must be known and understood in order to become a pilot is both vast and comprehensive. This process of learning and applying new information will continue throughout your career. You never stop learning in aviation, and those who believe that they have everything figured out are *dangerously good*.

> The best pilots are those who are always open to learning something new. The most dangerous pilots are the ones who believe they have everything figured out.

The process of learning to fly begins in the classroom. Prior to strapping into the front seat of the airplane, you are required to complete a rigorous and comprehensive course of instruction commonly known as *ground school*. During this phase of training you are introduced to a broad array of topics such as the fundamentals of aerodynamics, meteorology, aircraft systems, flight rules and regulations, and the unique physiological demands associated with flying. Each subject contains specific elements of static knowledge you must learned *and* understand. You must not only grasp the concepts but also demonstrate the ability to apply what you have learned in real time. There is a big difference between simply knowing the principles of lift and drag and understanding how to apply them as you configure your aircraft for an approach. Flight safety doesn't depend solely on what you know or the grade you made on a test, but on your ability to apply what you have learned while you are strapped in to a moving aircraft.

Make it your goal to not only know the material presented during training, but also to understand how to apply it effectively. Knowledge is of little value if you lack the ability to understand what to do with it.

Those who fail to demonstrate a solid grasp of the static knowledge presented in ground school do not advance and are not given the opportunity to fly. The reason should be clear enough. Who wants to hand the keys to their airplane to someone who doesn't know how to operate it? Would you want to be a passenger on a flight whose pilots lacked a firm grasp of the essential fundamentals of flying?

The relationship between the mastery of a static body of knowledge and the experience of attending ground school in advance of being allowed to operate an aircraft is one that will continue throughout your career. Every time you move to a new airplane, a new seat position, or a new organization, you can expect a formal course of instruction prior to actual flight training. While the manner in which the material is presented and the selection of relevant topics may vary as a function of your situation (initial training in an aircraft system will typically be more detailed than that which is presented during recurrent training), the concept is the same, and so are the expectations. You have to demonstrate that you possess the requisite knowledge about the aircraft you are preparing to fly and the regulatory framework in which you will operate before you can advance to the simulator or flight deck. You must earn the right to strap in.

The knowledge you acquire in these ground school sessions is critical to your future success, and it is important that your desire be focused on full mastery (understanding) of the material and not only on what is necessary to pass the test. Passing tests is important and necessary but that isn't what keeps you alive.

Dynamic Knowledge

If aviation were an equation, static knowledge would represent the constants, and dynamic knowledge would be the variables. While static knowledge is comprised of the core principles that are unchanging, dynamic knowledge refers to those aspects of operational information that are subject to revision.

Dynamic knowledge refers to the myriad of ever-changing information for which you are responsible to operate in a safe and effective manner. There is and will forever be the requirement to be familiar with updates to policies and procedures and the addition of new equipment and technologies. Successful flight operations are an ongoing process of assimilating and applying what you know with what you will continue to learn. The amount of information you will be required to know, update, and apply can be overwhelming at times, and there will be occasions when the temptation to stay with what you are comfortable with will be strong. In these moments, such reasoning will be buttressed by your track record of success with the old procedures. Why learn a new way when the old one works just fine? While I certainly understand this temptation, especially in those moments when long-established policies or procedures are revised with little or no explanation as to the specific benefits they will offer, there is a bigger issue at play when this type of mental resistance is indulged. The decision to embrace a posture of operational defiance that elevates your own preferences above those set forth by governing agencies is that of the Rebel. The desire to embrace this mindset strengthens in proportion to the number of accident or incident-free hours you have accumulated in your logbook, as your experience and success will conspire to convince you that your way is "good enough." These two words are the enemy of safety and effectiveness, and to the extent you find yourself using them on a regular basis, you are on your way to becoming *dangerously good*.

> In aviation, "good enough" is neither good nor enough. Aspire to a higher standard for yourself and require the same for your crew.

Let's look at some examples of how to apply dynamic knowledge in a manner that counters the temptation to succumb to a "good enough" mindset.

1. Be current. The pace at which revisions to policies and procedures and the introduction of new technologies occurs lends credence to the feeling of "drinking from a firehose." All at once there is much to know and remember and seemingly much more to learn. While the volume of these changes seems overwhelming at times, the bottom line is that it is the responsibility of each pilot to be up to date and compliant with regard to the most current directives. You will hear references to "maintaining currency" throughout your career, and these are not reminders to save your money, but rather references to your responsibility to ensure that you are applying the most recent and therefore most reliable information and guidelines on every flight. Safety and crew effectiveness are undermined when anyone involved in the operation is utilizing information that is outdated and unreliable. When you show up for a flight prepared to operate on the basis of outdated guidance, this reflects poorly on your sense of personal responsibility and demonstrates a lack of regard for the other members of your crew who are counting on you to put forth your best effort. Think of each flight as a potluck dinner for which everyone prepares and brings a dish that contributes to a positive dining experience. When you show up prepared to operate in accordance with outdated policies and procedures, you are bringing leftovers to the meal.

2. Be judicious. While the amount of information for which you are responsible is broad and complex, simply having the knowledge is of little value to those who fail to apply it wisely. Knowledge alone is insufficient in your development as a pilot who aspires to command a crew of their own. The true measure of a leader lies in their ability to apply their knowledge in situations for which there are no rules or regulations upon which one can rely for specific guidance. Like life, aviation is too complex and nuanced to rely on simple formulas to guide important decisions. Wisdom requires the timely application of what you know in the context of what is happening and is an acquired trait that comes with experience and a willingness to learn from your mistakes. Wisdom adds insight and discernment to the things you know and provides discretion with regard to practical application. As an example, in a subsequent chapter on the topic of communication we will discuss specific strategies that have proven to be effective in resolving interpersonal conflict. This is an important skill, as years of data have indicated that unresolved conflict on the flight deck creates an environment that inhibits the free and open flow of critical information between members of the crew. When this happens, a threat to safety has been introduced, and the crew is at greater risk for operational misfortune. In these circumstances, simply knowing the steps necessary to resolve conflict is insufficient if you lack the judgment necessary to determine when and where to engage with the other person. Wisdom requires discernment and discretion and the absence of these qualities will result in decisions that undermine flight safety.

> Like life, aviation is far too complex to rely on simple formulas to guide your decisions. Wisdom requires the ability to read between the lines of life's instruction manuals.

Personal and professional experience are valuable tools necessary for developing the wisdom that forges the important bond between what you know and how to best apply it. You won't always get things right, and you must be open to that reality. Mistakes are part of the learning process, and the pathway to wisdom is formed in the process of allowing your missteps to instruct and guide your development. Those who refuse to acknowledge their own mistakes or seek to place blame elsewhere are choosing to embrace a mindset that will handicap their growth.

A critical component of this process includes the establishment of realistic expectations. Pilots tend to be type A, can-do people whose high opinion of their abilities often makes it difficult to acknowledge and admit to mistakes, and many labor under the burden of a self-imposed expectation of perfection. To the extent this is the standard you have set for yourself, you will be locked into a closed loop of frustration. Excellence is the goal, not perfection. Excellence is attainable, while perfection is an illusion.

The wisdom required to one day command a crew includes a willingness to admit mistakes and use them as opportunities to learn and improve. The quest for perfection teaches you to see mistakes as threats to the image you seek to cultivate and will prompt a desire to deny or deflect responsibility.

> Excellence is a personal goal whose pursuit is both worthy and realistic. The quest for perfection is neither.

It is through the experience of learning, failing, and learning again that you develop the skills necessary to operate with and ultimately lead others effectively. Wisdom comes through the process of learning how to apply your acquired knowledge with discernment and discretion, and experience is life's classroom for the development of this valuable skill.

One of experience's most accomplished instructors is mistakes. You will make plenty of them along the way, and it is important to understand the significance of having the proper mindset with regard to their presence on your flight deck. Those who aspire to excellence see mistakes as tutors from which much can be learned and applied in the pursuit of improvement. This is the mindset of one who is teachable, and it is the teachable who are more inclined to excel.

Mastery of static and dynamic knowledge are fundamental to your success as an aviator. Not knowing the rules that govern your operations and being unable—or unwilling—to apply them appropriately are corrosive to the operation and all involved. Those who fail to stay current on the required knowledge or demonstrate resistance to learning from their mistakes are neglecting their responsibility. Both are preventable operational cancers that threaten flight safety if not diagnosed and treated.

Using a metaphor from team sports: don't show up with your uniform on if you have not taken the time to prepare yourself to give your best effort. Successful execution on the field demands that each player knows what is required on any given play, and ongoing development as a team requires an equal level of commitment from each player.

Your crew has the expectation that you will fulfill your role to the best of your ability and they invest a high level of trust in this expectation. This trust begins with knowing your stuff and is the basis of the cohesion necessary to operate effectively as a crew. Failures that are the result of poor procedural execution can be remedied through practice and repetition, but those resulting from inattention or negligence will sabotage any chance for excellence. Be mindful of your responsibility to maintain currency, and be consistent in your determination to ensure compliance. It is what others are expecting, and it is what you must expect of yourself.

Skill—Endeavor to Do Your Job with Excellence

Any mention of skill in the context of flying infers a reference to a pilot's ability to maneuver the aircraft with the precision necessary to meet the goals of safety, legality, and reliability. This is especially the case for the captain, whose responsibility it is to ensure that these operational goals are pursued in their proper order.

Anyone can be the captain when the weather is good and everything is working as it should, and in those instances your role is more like that of an in-flight manager. Captains are made in the moments when difficult circumstances require sound judgment and solid decision-making. Those who have participated in organized sports know that the ability to simultaneously manage the game plan, the clock, and unforeseen variables such as injuries or penalties requires skills that exceed those associated with the artful execution of X's and O's outlined in the playbook. Aviation is much the same in that the flying skills you develop and master in the training environment are tested and honed during the real-life operational encounters that can't be replicated in a classroom or flight simulator. Operational challenges are the moments that refine your individual and crew skills, and a thorough debrief at the end of each flight offers a perfect opportunity to learn from your experience. Unlike the classroom where the lesson comes before the test, it is often the case in aviation that you are tested first and then have the occasion to download the lesson.

> Anyone can be the captain when things are going smoothly. Challenging situations test your skills in ways that can provide the teachable moments that result in growth.

Skill and preparation are critical spokes on the Crew Wheel that will determine whether you contribute to or detract from the safety of the operation. Some of the most productive experiences I had during my years as a captain came as a result of time spent in conversation with individuals from maintenance, dispatch, and the loading crews during which I asked them questions about the pressures and procedures that guided their efforts. Not only did I find out more about how the pieces of the operation worked together than I ever learned in ground school, but these conversations were also beneficial in promoting a greater level of mutual respect and understanding between us. The fact that a captain would take the time to enter their world to learn and understand their challenges and limitations meant a great deal to them, and this process went a long way toward eliminating tribal barriers that can easily develop within an organization. Some may hesitate to any inclusion of the word *skill* in the description of this process, but I remain convinced that as a result of these conversations, I learned how to engage with the members of my extended operations team in a productive manner. Developing this type of working relationship requires a willingness to go beyond the boundaries of the assumptions that have been developed and reinforced by seeing the operation from only one perspective. This is a social skill, and its development and practice are critical to your effectiveness as a captain. Social skills require the ability to see and live beyond yourself and your own beliefs and perspectives and begin with a willingness to treat every person in the organization with the dignity they are owed as an individual and a member of the team. Take the time to see them as individuals first and members of a specific group second, and purpose to treat them as people rather than as parts of the operational machinery. Being a professional is more than giving the label to yourself and requires the additional effort to learn how to interact effectively with other members of the organization. A true professional lives, works, and aspires to see beyond the framework of their own job description. Professionals take the time to engage with and actively listen to the inputs and perspectives of other members of the team. Professionals are curious and teachable and are willing to engage with those outside their particular tribal affiliation. Strive to be known as a professional.

> A true professional aspires to live, work, and see beyond the framework of their own job description.

LEADERSHIP

Chapter 5

Be Command Oriented

Know the Expectations of Leadership

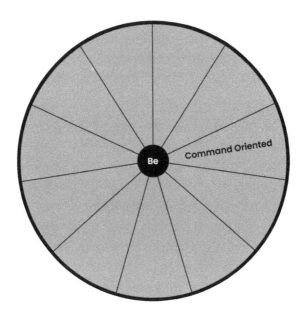

The Mindset of a Leader

Much has been written and presented over the years about the qualities that define what it means to be a leader and for some its overuse has undermined a clear understanding of what it looks like in practice. I can remember being asked during an airline interview to define what it means to be a leader. Though I had heard the word numerous times and had been instructed in the importance of being one, I had never been asked to offer a description of its specific qualities. I remember thinking about the question for a moment and then saying, *"Leaders hold themselves to high standards of performance and accountability and inspire others to follow their example. Leaders are confident, approachable, and skilled at motivating others to give their best effort."* That's a pretty good on-demand definition and I'm convinced that it helped carry the day as the interviewers seem pleased and I got the job. I've thought about my answer over the years and in that time I haven't changed my mind about the fundamentals of leadership.

> If something is worth doing, it is worth doing to the very best of your ability. This is the mindset of a professional. "Good enough" is not an acceptable standard for a professional.

In aviation, leadership and professionalism go hand in hand and to the extent you embrace the traits and skills outlined in this book you will earn the right to wear both labels. On a fundamental level, the character traits you embrace will determine how you understand and exercise command authority. Your leadership style will reflect the strength of your character. This book does not offer step-by-step instruction on the things you must do to become a professional crew member and captain but instead encourages you to be the kind of person whose character and behavior are consistent with the pursuit of excellence. If it is your desire to *do* the things that define what it means to be a leader you must first *aspire to be* a person who values the principles outlined in this book.

> Don't think of these principles as things you must do, but rather as qualities consistent with what kind of person you want to be. Who you are will determine what you do.

Given that much of the material in this book deals with leadership principles, some may conclude that this guidance don't yet apply to them. You may believe that as a first officer, you lack the official capacity or opportunity to exercise leadership. I strongly disagree with this conclusion and believe that opportunities for leadership exist in the common circumstances of life.

Whenever you find yourself in a position that affords the opportunity to exercise influence over others, you have the opportunity to demonstrate leadership. Providing wise guidance and direction to those who need it is the essence of what it means to be a leader. Think of the people in your life over whom you have the opportunity to exert influence or present yourself as an example to emulate. This could be a younger sibling, a coworker, or the new kid at school. In each instance, you have knowledge and experience that they lack. You know things they don't, and you have the opportunity to decide what to do about it. As I see it, you have three options about how to handle such situations:

- You can opt not to share what you know, let others try to figure things out independently, and simply observe as they struggle. This is an example of *passive leadership,* and no one is served when it is employed. Passive leadership is characterized by an unwillingness to take initiative to solve problems. Passive leaders would rather pretend a problem doesn't exist than take the necessary steps to resolve it.

- You can provide help if and when it is requested. *Reactive leadership* is more likely to engage in problem solving than its passive cousin, but only when forced to and typically with a minimum amount of effort. Reactive leadership is content to address immediate concerns than pursue lasting solutions and does little to foster a collective sense of unity and purpose. Like a vending machine, reactive leadership stands alone in silent isolation and is content to engage on an as-needed basis.

- You can choose to voluntarily offer guidance and assistance for the benefit of the individual and the team as a whole. *Proactive leaders* see a need and take action to pursue solutions that benefit not only the organization but also its individual members. *Proactive leadership* is more committed to serving than being served.

I would hope that we can all agree that option three is most consistent with the character and heart of a leader. A leader's interest must extend beyond themselves and be demonstrated by a willingness to use their influence to be of service to someone else. You'll notice I said *influence and not authority*. Sometimes leadership opportunities happen organically as a by-product of finding yourself in a position to do something for the benefit of another simply because you have access to knowledge or resources they lack. You don't have to have a title in order to show leadership. At its core, leadership is a mindset focused on taking initiative to balance the interests of the organization and its individual members.

The point I am making is this. Your leadership training is already underway. To the extent that you capitalize on the opportunities that are presented in your everyday life—at school, at home, or at your current job—to help guide and direct others in ways that advance their personal or professional growth and development, you are exercising leadership.

In the process, you are also cultivating the attitude of one whose commitment to service will equip you to one day exercise your command authority in a manner that enhances crew performance, morale, and flight safety. People respond most positively when they believe that those in authority over them have a sincere interest in their welfare.

> Proactive flying requires the participation and engagement of professionals who are committed to the exercise of proactive leadership.

Take this as a challenge and make it part of your training on and off the flight deck to become a proactive leader. Demonstrate genuine care and concern about others as you offer the guidance and direction they need to grow and develop. In your encounters with others, be mindful that what you say, how you treat them, and the genuine regard you show for their welfare will be scrutinized, evaluated, and absorbed. You may well be shaping and teaching others in ways that aren't immediately recognizable. Your interaction with those who look to you for guidance will likely influence the composition of their mental composite sketch of what a leader looks like. Make it your leadership SOP to treat others with dignity as you guide their efforts in the pursuit of common objectives. That means everybody. Afford them the same respect and consideration you would want to receive.

> The SOP of a proactive leader values serving over being served. The best leaders put the interests of others above their own.

One of the most important and memorable leadership lessons I learned occurred shortly after I joined my first tactical navy squadron. Though I had been in the navy for five years at this time, this was my first experience being deployed aboard an aircraft carrier. I joined the squadron while it was already on station in the Mediterranean, and was overwhelmed by the learning curve that lay before me as I attempted to absorb the myriad of practical and operational aspects of life at sea. Fortunately for me, a fellow aviator in the squadron recognized my confusion and showed me the ropes of even the most basic aspects of everyday life aboard ship. (He later told me I looked like a dog trying to understand what was being said on the radio, and it reminded him of how he felt during his first days and weeks at sea.) No one ordered him to do this—I wasn't his assignment, and he certainly had no extra time in his schedule to babysit the new guy. But he did it anyway. He was willing to offer guidance to someone who needed both, and he didn't hesitate to be of service. He was younger than me and lower in rank but his experience and willingness to volunteer his time were of greater importance. He knew what I needed to know and was unselfish with his time as he taught me what I needed to understand to succeed and stay alive.

Such is the mindset and the conduct of a proactive leader. These leaders are given to be of service to others rather than motivated by a desire to be served or sought for favors. Be the kind of person inclined to show initiative in assisting and equipping others with the tools they need to succeed, and you will be well on your way to being a respected leader.

Note: A willingness to assist and equip others applies to the things they *can't* do for themselves rather than what they *won't* do. A significant component of the art of leadership is developing the discernment to differentiate between these two types of people. Wisdom and discernment are developed through experience, and you'll likely get played along the way as you encounter people who persuade you that they *can't* when it becomes clear that they just *won't*. Don't beat yourself up when this happens—we've all been there. Learn from experience and apply your lessons the next time you have a déjà vu flashback with someone else. There is no limit to what some people will allow you to do for them. *Proactive leaders* are also teachable. While passive and reactive leaders seek to avoid interpersonal turbulence, proactive leaders are willing to engage in difficult conversations. *Proactive leaders* move toward problems rather than away from them.

Our attitudes and beliefs about the nature of leadership are developed and reinforced well before we have been vested with the legal right to exercise authority over others. For most of us, leadership training began in school or at home as we observed the manner in which those in command of our lives exercised authority. These organic leadership laboratories offered both positive and negative examples of how authority should and should not be exercised. We were drawn to those whose leadership styles inspired us to give our best effort to the task and the team and repulsed by those who wanted to ensure that we never lost sight of our shortcomings. We took mental notes along the way, and many of us made pledges to ourselves about what we would or wouldn't do when it came our time to exercise authority over others. Perhaps your vow went something like this: *"When I'm a boss/parent I'll never say (or do)* _____."

Spoiler alert: Though many of us make similar pledges regarding what we vow *never* to say or do, the day comes when we find ourselves violating this sacred oath. The first time you hear forbidden words and phrases come out of your mouth, you will stop dead in your tracks and ponder the issues in play at that moment as you work through the fear of having become your mother or father. Take heart in the fact that while such an occasion is almost a certainty, it can also be a teachable moment, as you have the opportunity to reconsider the wisdom of that which you once dismissed out of hand. This was certainly the case in my life, and as I grew older and had kids of my own, I realized that my parents had become much smarter with time.

Acquiring an understanding of leadership in the social laboratory of our interactions with and observations of others is a common practice—one that results in the creation of our own interpretations of the nature of leadership. As a result of this experience, many of us develop a subjective mental construct of what a leader looks like and how they should or should not behave in a given situation. Over the years, we create the equivalent of a mental police composite sketch of what a leader looks like. For many who have drawn such an image, a majority of its defining characteristics are based on negative attributes. As such, the leadership qualities that define these sketches can be strongly biased in the direction of avoiding the types of interpersonal dynamics that make you feel denigrated and disrespected in your own life. In other words, this social laboratory teaches us a lot about what kind of leaders we *don't* want to become, and these lessons can be deeply ingrained into our memories for years.

The emotional imprints of these negative experiences often make big dents in our memories that serve to establish our basis of understanding regarding the nature of leadership. They are usually the catalysts for the oaths we swear to ourselves about what we won't do when we are promoted to a position of authority. To the extent your leadership philosophy is built on avoiding a replay of the difficult lessons of the past, you are more likely to be a passive or reactive leader. The attempt to distance yourself from bad memories will can train you to evade unpleasant situations in the present. This is a self-serving strategy that will translate to weak and ineffective leadership. Let me urge you not to dwell too deeply on the things you don't want to be but rather to use these memory dents to steer you in the direction of what you want to become. Let the recollection of mistreatment by people in authority be the impetus for a commitment to treating those under your command with dignity and respect. Use your negative experiences to prompt you in the right direction rather than as a tool for avoiding destructive behaviors. It's a subtle but significant shift.

> Focus your attention on who you want to be rather than on who you want to avoid becoming.

Devote your attention to developing the character traits and qualities that equip you to become a more skilled and proactive leader than the ones you worked for, as opposed to making a conscious effort to avoid becoming just like them. The former pursuit cultivates a healthy attitude toward your interactions with others. The latter mindset is more likely to result in the creation of a template of avoidance that restricts the boundaries of your leadership style. Looking forward to what you want to become is the way of teachability and growth. Looking backward to distance yourself from potential mistakes is the way of limitation and cultivates a stunted leadership style based on fear of failure.

I call this *rearview mirror leadership*. Imagine that as you drive along the road you are preoccupied with looking backward to avoid potholes on the pavement behind you. This greatly increases the likelihood of running off the road and I know people who have run their lives into a ditch because of their fixation on what was behind them. This misplaced focus jeopardizes not only the operation of the car but also the safety of its occupants. In this instance, others depend on you to operate wisely and prudently to get everyone to the planned destination. The more you focus your attention on scanning the rearview mirror as the car moves down the highway, the more others will lose confidence in your ability to get to the destination safely and the more hesitant they will be about getting in the car with you in the future. To the extent this becomes your driving philosophy, many will look for another ride as they become convinced that you are not invested in their welfare. The bottom line of this analogy is that one of the core principles of leadership is demonstrating concern for the welfare of those under your command. This is not something that can be forged with nominal gestures on your part. People can smell disingenuous interest from afar, and the aroma is never pleasant. For this reason, your philosophy of leadership must effectively balance the goals of the organization with the interests and well-being of those under your command.

Leadership is rooted in your attitude about what it means to exercise influence or authority over others. This begins with an awareness of our ability to influence performance and morale with our words and our conduct. Be proactive in your commitment to treat others with dignity and respect. This means everyone. Don't be a dent in someone else's memory. Make it a practice to remember their names, ask about their stories, and take time to listen rather than simply waiting for the opportunity to tell them about yourself. Don't be quick to render judgment on that which you don't understand or can't appreciate. These are traits of proactive leaders, and one need not wait to be in a position of authority to exercise them. You can begin right now, where you are, in the context of everyday interactions with others. When ordering from a fast-food counter, take note of the server's name and use it in your exchange with them. Ask them how their day is going, and engage with them in a conversational tone rather than as someone reciting a list of desires. Treat them as real people and not as servants who exist to cater to your needs. This is a practical example of how to develop a mindset of treating others with respect and doesn't require a checklist of action items. Try it out the next few times you find yourself next in line to order food. It won't take any extra time, and I think you will be amazed at the responses you get from those who have become accustomed to being treated as accessories rather than as individuals. This is an essential part of your CRM and leadership training.

> Let the poor leadership examples of others be your teacher, but refuse to let them become your guide. Don't lead from the shadow of someone else's mistakes.

My desire to become a pilot came about as a result of just such an experience. Someone took the initiative to do something on my behalf and in the process, introduced me to a brand-new world that captured both my interest and my imagination. My first trip on an airplane was also my most consequential. The trip was a grueling flight from Travis Air Force Base in California to Kadena Air Base on the island of Okinawa on a Pan Am DC-6. We made fuel stops on both Midway and Wake Island, and the trip seemed to take forever. I was five years old and was traveling with my mom and my one-year-old sister to join my father, who was stationed at Kadena with the air force.

I remember well the particular moment on that flight that charted the course of my life. A pretty lady in a blue suit with wings on her jacket came to our row and winked at my mom as she asked if "anyone here would like to go and see the cockpit." My mom said I was out of the seat before she could say anything, and off I went to the front of the airplane with the nice lady. I'll never forget the exhilaration of walking through the cockpit door and being captivated by the array of switches and gauges that seemed to cover everything but the windows. The crew introduced themselves as they welcomed me aboard, kindly and patiently told me about the various instruments, and answered my questions in a way that made sense to a five year old. I was hooked. I distinctly remember thinking, "This is what I want to be when I grow up." There was no looking back, and I never considered any other professional pursuit.

I've thought about this Pan Am crew a number of times over the years. Their simple act of kindness to someone else's five-year-old was a seismic event in a young boy's life that directed his future steps. There was no way they could ever fully appreciate the significance of this moment and the impact they had made. They had used their position of influence to introduce an impressionable child to a new world of possibilities and had done so in a way that made him want to emulate them and pursue their profession. I could argue that my aviation career began on the flight deck of that DC-6, not because that's where I learned how to fly an airplane. Rather, that was where I discovered what I wanted to do and who I wanted to be. I wanted to be like those pilots. After that experience, I always had a soft spot in my heart for Pan Am, and the news of their bankruptcy in 1991 was like reading the obituary of an old friend.

The more I've reflected upon the significance of that event, the more I have come to appreciate the degree to which everyone who wears the uniform has the opportunity to influence the thoughts, perceptions, and motivations of others. Ours is a conspicuous profession for which people have a high level of trust and respect. I would encourage you to remember this each time you put on your uniform. As you walk through the terminal or around the base in your uniform and in your encounters with the public, be ever mindful of the fact that, in all likelihood you will be in the company of people who want to be convinced that their respect for you and your profession is warranted. Furthermore, never lose sight of the memory of being a wide-eyed kid who once looked at pilots with rock-star respect and marveled at the possibility of being just like them one day. On any given day, chances are good that you will cross paths with a kid imagining the same dream. Wear your uniform with pride, and conduct yourself with courtesy and decorum in every encounter. No matter how many reroutes you've had or how frustrated you are with crew scheduling a true professional can never be too busy to be courteous and respectful. You are an ambassador for the profession and your company. Don't ever allow yourself to be the reason people lose respect for the profession or interest in their pursuit of the dream of being just like you one day.

> Pursue excellence and not perfection. Excellence is attainable and worthy of pursuit, while perfection is neither. The pursuit of excellence motivates and inspires. A quest for perfection breeds frustration.

Exercising leadership is a fluid and dynamic process for which there are too many variables to construct a list of rules that guarantee success. That isn't how life works, and some of the most frustrated people I have known are those who seek to govern their lives according to a strict code of conduct that makes no provision for individual judgment. As is the case with flight operations, being an effective leader requires an ability to be skilled at both symphony and jazz.

There is no shortage of rules in any complex operation, and aviation is certainly no exception. It is important to understand, however, that there can't possibly be a rule or procedure for every situation you encounter in life or in aviation. For this reason, wisdom, judgment, and feedback from others are critical ingredients for equipping you to manage and resolve situations for which there is no clear guidance or precedent.

It is for this reason that the crew and leadership skills offered in this book should be considered as principles and guidelines rather than a recipe of specific dos and don'ts that can be applied in any circumstances.

> When you are the captain, few will remember how well you landed the airplane, but none will forget how you treated them or what it was like to work for you.

It has been estimated that 60–75 percent of people in leadership positions in the US are considered to be poor or ineffective leaders by both the organization for which they work and those who serve under their authority. These percentages are consistent across organizations of varying size and complexity, and the primary factors that contribute to this percentage fall into two categories:

1. *Poorly defined expectations*—This refers to a situation in which the person in charge lacks a clear understanding of exactly what they are supposed to be doing. In some instances this fundamental lack of awareness occurs when someone is promoted to a position above their ability and in others is attributable to a lack of specific guidance from the organization about expectations for their new role. Yes, they have been given a job description and perhaps even a briefing or a week of classroom training on their duties and responsibilities, but it is usually the case that a course of formal instruction does not automatically translate to the level of preparation necessary for success. In many instances, this disconnect between classroom instruction and practical realities is magnified by a reluctance on the part of the new manager to ask for help or clarification for fear of appearing to be unqualified or unprepared.

When clarity is absent many who are promoted to a position of leadership will resign themselves to figuring it out as they go and faking it in the meantime to present a veneer of competence and confidence.

I can recall such an instance in my own life and the leadership train wreck that ensued as a result of my unwillingness to ask for instruction regarding the expectations associated with a new leadership role. I was a junior officer who had just been assigned to be a Division Officer in the Maintenance Department of my squadron. The navy rotates their pilots through an assortment of positions within the squadron as a means of providing the opportunity to become familiar with all aspects of the squadron's operation. This was a training program designed to equip junior officers with the tools to one day command a squadron of their own. The division over which I now had supervision was responsible for the maintenance of electronics, communications, and navigation systems for our aircraft and the person who held the position before me was another junior officer who had been on the job for about six months. My training for this new role consisted of a twenty-minute briefing that provided a general overview of the key players and a heads-up about looming deadlines for various reports and personnel evaluations. That was it. I remember him asking me at the end if I had any questions, and though I had plenty, I responded reflexively with an assurance that I had none. "I got this," was my reply. Pride eclipsed my judgment in that moment and in the months to follow as I embraced the naval motto of, "Better to die than to look bad," as I pretended to know things that I didn't. I was less of a leader than a name on the organizational chart and was ineffective with regard to my contribution to the squadron and my support for those under my supervision. Fortunately for me, a wise and senior chief petty officer recognized my plight and took it upon himself to teach me how to exercise my authority with wisdom, humility, and a willingness to admit when I needed help. I'll never forget the day when this man who was old enough to be my father and had been in the navy during the days when I was playing Little League baseball took me aside and asked if he could share a couple of things with me. *"Sir,"* he said, *"it's better to ask for help with the things you don't know than it is to pretend that you know them. Let me help you. You fly, and I'll help you navigate."* I'll never forget these words and the mentor-student relationship they initiated. The chief's words were concise, accurate, and timely and were offered with the demeanor of one who was willing to invest in the growth and development of another. Thus began my enrollment in a hands-on leadership laboratory in which I learned more in a matter of months than I ever could have learned from a lifetime of classroom presentations. The lessons I learned from this chief stuck with me and I will be forever indebted to him for his willingness to mentor the new boss. Among the many lessons he taught me was the importance of asking questions of those with more knowledge and experience rather than attempting to present a level of comprehension and competence that I did not possess. I also learned the value of owning my mistakes and taking personal responsibility for the missteps for which I alone was accountable. An important motto I embraced during this significant period was this: "When you mess up, fess up."

> It is better to ask for help with the things you don't know than it is to pretend to know them. Those under your command can smell incompetence, and this aroma is not enhanced by the practice of faking it.

People who pretend to know what they don't are serving the best interests of no one. You may fool yourself and comfort your ego with assurances of your competence and qualifications, but no one else is playing the game. Those under your command can smell incompetence, and the aroma is not enhanced by the practice of faking it.

> Fess up when you mess up. Own your mistakes. Hiding them will stunt your development as a leader.

2. Lack of Performance Feedback—There is an old saying that "no news is good news," and unfortunately this has become a metric used by many to determine the quality of their performance. Every professional wants a measure of assurance that they are doing a good job and that their performance is up to the standards set forth by the organization. Lest there be any doubt as to the truthfulness of this statement, think about the level of anticipation and anxiety you experience as you await the verdict of your evaluator at the completion of a check ride or an exam. *"How did I do?"* is the question on everyone's mind at that moment, and it is often the case that we can't fully hear or process the details of a debrief until we have been given the assurance that we passed. In aviation, evaluations are a regular fact of life, and in those moments we have the opportunity to gain insight into our performance and draw conclusions regarding our overall level of proficiency and professionalism. It is also the case that in these instances, we are more likely to perform at levels that exceed our everyday efforts. This is understandable, as we not only want to pass the check ride, but are also invested in ensuring that our reputation is not tarnished in the process. An actor who knows that a renowned drama critic will attend a specific show will be more likely to apply an added measure of attention to their role for this particular performance. It's in the nature of us all. Our performance is influenced as a function of who is watching, and when that someone is in a position to offer or withhold a special measure of approval, we are more motivated to give our best.

What about those moments, however, when no one whose validation you seek is watching? Given that this is more the norm than the exception with most endeavors, it is easy to assume a posture of complacency and rely on silence as our primary performance metric. By silence, I mean the absence of specific feedback regarding the quality of our performance. This silence not only refers to the lack of positive feedback, but also the negative. It is also in our nature to conclude that an absence of negative feedback must mean that I'm doing a good job. In this model, no complaints = well done.

The regular evaluations for which you are likely to invest a level of effort that exceeds that of your everyday performance is an insufficient metric by which you can measure your effectiveness as a leader and as a professional. These are snapshots that point to a particular moment in time when you aspired to excel and are not always a lasting reflection of your performance.. It is for this reason that I strongly encourage you to participate in a debrief at the conclusion of each flight, real or simulated. Debriefs are useful exercises for obtaining the feedback that can translate into practical steps for improvement. In a debrief of this nature, everyone is both a teacher and a student. Teachability is a necessary quality for effective leadership, and those who resist the opportunity to learn are faking it in a way that will make them dangerously good captains.

Authority and Leadership

Years of data obtained from accident investigations and safety audits in the aviation industry has demonstrated one indisputable fact: flight safety is enhanced when captains exercise their authority with wisdom and judgment. While the captain's exercise of command authority will develop and mature with time and experience, it is essential that this growth is grounded in a fundamental understanding of the nature of the authority that has been vested by the company and the FAA. Let's begin this discussion of the captain's authority with a simple question:

The pilot in command has full authority on the flight deck. Does having authority make someone a good leader?

Understanding the difference between leadership and authority and their application to the dynamics of a flight crew is critical to knowing how to apply the leadership spokes of the Crew Wheel. Authority gives the captain the legal right to have the final say in the operation of the aircraft while leadership refers to the manner in which this authority is exercised.

Authority gives you the power to command the operation of the aircraft and the actions of the crew, but having authority does not automatically mean you are an effective leader. Leadership is both the art and science of exercising your authority in a manner that inspires others to give their best in the pursuit of organizational goals. Before we explore the specific qualities associated with effective leadership, let's take a closer look at the topic of authority.

Captain is a title that is commonly used to identify the ranking member of the flight crew, but it is not the word used by the FAA to identify the person in command of the aircraft and crew. The FAA instead uses the term *Pilot In Command (PIC)* to establish and outline the tenets of what it means to exercise authority on the flight deck. Incidentally, while the airlines typically use the term *First Officer, or FO,* to identify the person who is the immediate subordinate to the captain, the FAA refers to this individual as the *Second In Command (SIC).*

Let's look at the Federal Aviation Regulations (FAR) that establish the authority of the captain/PIC.

FAR 91.3

a. The pilot in command of an aircraft is directly responsible for, and is the final authority as to, the operation of that aircraft.

b. In an in-flight emergency requiring immediate action, the pilot in command may deviate from any rule of this part to the extent required to meet that emergency.

c. Each pilot in command who deviates from a rule under paragraph (b) of this section shall, upon the request of the Administrator, send a written report of that deviation to the Administrator.

As part (a) clearly states, the PIC has the ultimate and final authority to determine how the aircraft is operated. This means that the buck stops in the left seat. Part (b) gives the PIC the latitude to deviate from written rules and regulations in emergency situations. An example of this would be a captain's decision to exceed the maximum speed of 250 KTS below 10,000 FT in an emergency situation. Part (b) authorizes the captain to exercise judgment and discretion to violate this rule in the interest of getting a disabled aircraft on the ground expeditiously.

Part (c) introduces the element of accountability and makes it clear that decisions to violate the rules in accordance with paragraph (b) must be explained to the satisfaction of the FAA. Captains are authorized to deviate from established guidelines in emergency situations and are expected to exercise sound judgment in the pursuit of the safest course of action in these situations. In no case is the captain authorized to operate outside established operational guidelines as a matter of preference or convenience. Accountability is a necessary backstop to the exercise of authority in any organization, and allowing someone to operate without it is a recipe for allowing authority to become tyranny. Lest there be any doubt as to whom you are accountable in the exercise of your PIC authority, you need only look at the FAA logo on your pilot's license and the company logo on your ID badge and aircraft. Both entities confer the legal authority to command the aircraft, and reserve the right to establish guidelines and demand accountability for the manner in which it is exercised.

FAR 121.537

d. Each pilot in command of an aircraft is, during flight time, in command of the aircraft and crew and is responsible for the safety of the passengers, crew members, cargo, and aircraft. The pilot in command has full control and authority in the operation of the aircraft, without limitation, over other crew members and their duties during flight time, whether or not he holds valid certificates authorizing him to perform the duties of those crew members.

e. Each pilot in command of an aircraft is responsible for the preflight planning and the operation of the flight in compliance with this chapter and the operations specifications.

This section of FAR part 121 echoes the provisions of aircraft control outlined in part 91 and expands the authority of the PIC to include other members of the crew. As such, the PIC is the final authority with regard to all matters pertaining to the safe and legal operation of the flight, and their operational decisions are binding. This isn't to negate the requirement or desirability of input from the crew when making decisions, but to establish the ultimate rung on the ladder of responsibility. Examples of this would be the decision to add extra gas during the flight planning phase or to deviate around a line of thunderstorms enroute. Both situations would involve discussion among the crew, but the ultimate decision as to the proper course of action is up to the captain.

Company flight manuals contain similar language that outlines the captain's authority and at times specify the manner in which it can be exercised. For example, in conditions of low visibility or high winds, your company will identify specific conditions in which the captain is required to make a takeoff or landing. In many instances your company's flight operations manual contains policy and procedural guidelines on topics already covered by the FARs. In these instances, the provisions outlined in a company's flight operations manual may be *more* restrictive than the FARs, but never *less* so. While the FAA and the company for whom you fly clearly establish the captain's legal authority in matters regarding the conduct of the flight, it is incumbent on each captain to exercise their command in a manner that earns the trust and confidence of the crew. Having the authority to command doesn't make you a leader. How you understand and exercise your authority does.

> Having the authority to command doesn't make you a leader. How you understand and apply your authority is the essence of leadership.

The captain is the primary focal point of the operation and is expected to exercise authority in a manner that ensures the safe, legal, and reliable operation of the flight. The captain is the person whose attitude and actions most influence the performance of the crew. With that in mind, take a closer look at the degree to which your attitude determines your understanding of what it means to be a leader. I call this the *Attitude of Command.*

> Think back to our definition of CRM. The captain *Manages* the *Crew* and all available *Resources* for the benefit of the operation.

The Attitude of Command

The *Attitude of Command* is a blend of thoughts and opinions that reflect both your understanding of what it means to be vested with the legal authority to command, and the manner in which this authority should be exercised. Just as skilled flying requires more than the ability to recall procedures from memory, knowing how to lead people involves a level of discernment that can't be developed simply by reading and understanding an outline. Effective leaders must be adept at understanding the nuances associated with human interaction and also discerning in their application of the traits and qualities that comprise the spokes of the Crew Wheel.

Your attitude of command establishes your priorities with regard to whose interests are most important—your own, those of the organization, or those under your command. Managing the tension associated with balancing these competing interests is a key aspect of the art of leadership and begins with a consideration of your personal attitude about the nature of authority and leadership. Your *Attitude of Command* translates into the methods and behaviors that characterize and define your leadership style. Those who fail to consider the impact of their attitude and behaviors on others lack the character necessary for wise and appropriate leadership. Character is a critical ingredient to establishing and maintaining a proper *Attitude of Command* and the "Be" aspects of the individual spokes of the Crew Wheel are intended to underscore the importance of this point. Good character is a critical component of the job description of a leader and is essential to the establishment of trust. If those under your command don't trust you, you won't be able to lead them. Solid character inspires the confidence of those under your command and creates a positive operational climate that enhances crew performance, job satisfaction, and morale. A lack of character on the part of the leader is a cancer that erodes all that is good and productive about the team. A captain without character will be more likely to transform the exercise of authority into exploitation and when this happens the trust of the crew can easily mutate into resentment. While someone can have character and integrity while lacking leadership skills, the reverse is never the case. It is not possible for effective leadership to be exercised by those who lack these qualities.

> Your attitude of command translates into the methods and behaviors that characterize and define your leadership style.

Your *Attitude of Command* is determined by two fundamental principles:

1. **How you view your role as a leader.** What is of greatest importance to me in my role as a leader? Meeting organizational goals? Taking care of the people under my command? Making sure that everyone in either camp is happy with my performance and my decisions?

2. **How you view the nature and importance of relationships with other people.** Do I view others as team members or as utilities the be used in the completion of a task?

These fundamental questions can be explored more completely through considering the primary emphasis that describes your mindset about the nature of authority and the exercise of leadership. Here are three areas of personal emphasis that will likely influence and shape your *Attitude of Command,* and to the extent any of these variables are over-emphasized your leadership will be ineffective.

- Emphasis on Results
- Emphasis on Position
- Emphasis on Popularity

Emphasis on Results – *"It's all about getting the job done."*

This is a leadership mindset characterized by a single-minded devotion to the accomplishment of organizational goals with scant consideration given to the welfare of its members. The job is all that matters, and people become necessary tools for achieving a particular objective. Members of the organization are valued and perhaps even esteemed when their performance meets the expectations of the leader and are equally subject to scorn and derision when it does not. Leaders who focus on task completion to the exclusion of all other considerations are given to seeing others as utilities more than individuals. As such, the degree to which members of the organization are afforded respect is based solely on their usefulness in the pursuit of stated objectives. A collective sense of frustration and burnout can develop when members of the team feel as though they are little more than pieces of the organizational machinery.

Leaders with an overdeveloped *Emphasis on Results* may find that the successes they realize comes at a significant cost in terms of the adverse impact on their relationships with others. The blindness that results from a leader's overdeveloped sense of drive and ambition can create an inability to recognize the interpersonal damage in their wake as they climb the proverbial ladder. When command decisions are made from the perspective of getting the job done without regard for the safety and welfare of those involved the value of the prize can be negated by the intangible costs associated with the quest. People need to be appreciated and made to feel like their efforts are valued. To the extent your attitude of command is characterized by an overemphasis on getting the job done with no regard for the welfare of those under your command, you are no longer leading them, you are using them, and this is how they will feel. While people with an overdeveloped *Emphasis on Results* are often recipients of awards and accolades from their organizations, these rewards often come at a high personal cost that won't be recognized until retirement. The day will come when people no longer call you captain, no one calls to ask for your advice, and the testimonials to your greatness are relegated to memorials hung on a forgotten wall that few will stop by to admire. It's possible that many of the people who once loved and supported you will have grown weary of always being a secondary concern to your pursuit of achievement and will have moved on. When the time comes that you are no longer on the active roster—and it does for us all—will it comfort you to know that your plaques and awards have come at the cost of relationships with others? What solace is there in knowing that the people who were once closest to you now lament that they no longer even know you? I've seen this happen many times, and the emotional fallout of such an ending is both sad and sobering. It doesn't have to be this way. Flying is a wonderful career, and I am forever grateful for having had the opportunity to do the only thing I ever wanted to do since I was a young boy, but let me caution you to avoid getting so caught up in the pursuit of advancement and accolades to the point that you lose sight of the contributions and support of others.

I once had a Commanding Officer (CO) in the navy whose leadership style made him the poster boy for an *Emphasis on Results*. His skill as an aviator and as a leader was handicapped by his desire to be known as the person who go results at any cost. He was a man who was going places. His motto was, "Results matter. Everything else is BS." Ever true to his words, he ruled the squadron with an iron fist, micromanaging his officers, publicly shaming those who failed to meet his expectations, and driving his enlisted people to exhaustion—all in a quest to be known by all as the best. Those who worked for him feared him, and not in a good way.

There is a type of fear that is based on a healthy degree of respect, and another that is rooted in a sense of dread. Healthy fear provides a framework of understanding and predictability regarding the nature of relationships with people and things that creates a sense of stability. Unhealthy fear, on the other hand, is ever mindful of the likelihood of doing something wrong and this stifles the desire to do more than the absolute minimum required for the task. Healthy fear understands and appreciates the rules and limitations associated with a situation and adapts as necessary, while unhealthy fear conditions people to anticipate the imposition of arbitrary and capricious punishments for performance that does not meet the expectations of the boss. In the eyes of the CO a failure to execute to perfection was considered weakness and no consideration was given to other factors. There were two standards of performance, perfection and failure, and the inability to achieve the former earned the distinction of being called the latter.

Needless to say, no one wanted to fly with the CO, and we all did our best to be invisible when he was around. We feared the wrath that came with the inability to achieve the perfection he demanded and his entry in the front door would prompt an exodus through the back as grown men scurried to avoid his gaze. Pay attention to the times when you get the sense that those under your command are avoiding you, and in these moments take inventory of your leadership skills and evaluate your *Attitude of Command.* It is oftentimes the case that the first indication of the need for an adjustment is the realization that the people who work for you no longer come to you for advice. As a leader, you are a shepherd who must study your flock and respond appropriately to changes in their habits and behaviors.

An overdeveloped *Emphasis on Results* can weaken your awareness of the importance of treating those around you with the respect and dignity they deserve.

Leaders motivated primarily by an *Emphasis on Results* often sacrifice those closest to them on the altar of their own ambition, and when such leaders look in the mirror, they see a boss. A boss is given to a one-dimensional view of their authority as being focused on driving others toward the achievement of a goal while demonstrating little or no regard for their welfare. A boss cares only that the goal is realized and expresses little consideration or appreciation for personal costs incurred by others in the pursuit of the objective. Getting the job done, whatever the cost, is *all* that matters. Leaders, on the other hand, are those who are committed to balancing the interests of the organization with those of its members. Be a leader not a boss.

Emphasis on Position – *"It's all about the prestige."*

Being the captain means having a position of trust, responsibility, and respectability. The stripes on your shoulders and sleeves give evidence of the fact that you are someone who is deserving of respect. For some, the primary satisfaction of having attained such a position is that of being known by others as someone of status. The prospect of having the legal authority to direct the entire show and all of the actors is almost intoxicating for some, and people for whom their rank becomes their identity are less interested in exercising leadership than they are in being known by their rank or title. I am always suspicious of those who insist on being addressed by their rank or title long after they have retired.

Abraham Lincoln once said that the true test of a person's character is to give them authority. It's been my observation that truer words were rarely spoken, and this adage reflects a great degree of insight into human nature. I have witnessed some remarkable individual transformations in people as they advanced from a position in the pack to that of the lead dog. The most notable changes involved people who were at one time reasonable and engaging and upon promotion to a position of authority morphed into petty and inflexible caricatures of themselves. In truth, these negative traits were probably always simmering just beneath the surface of their character, and the attainment of the power and status associated with command simply allowed that which was hidden from most to now become visible to all.

To the extent that your sense of personal and professional significance is derived from being known and acknowledged as someone who is both important and deserving of respect, your leadership style will be flavored by the need to be right and look good in the process. Your rank will become your identity, and when this happens, your desire for status and reputation will govern not only how you do your job, but also the manner in which you interact with others. Associations with people who have the ability to further your own interests will be pursued with great vigor, while interactions with people of lesser influence will be perfunctory at best. This variance with regard to your treatment of others is an indicator of your character.

Leaders whose primary motivation is to collect and polish their own trophies breed a level of contempt among their subordinates that can be quite corrosive to the morale and effectiveness of the unit. Leaders whose exercise of authority is primarily influenced by the need for recognition will easily deviate from the standards they require of others, and they often do so with no awareness of the contradiction. The quest for glory can afflict such people with a type of selective blindness that doesn't allow them to consider the fact that everyone around them is not as personally invested in their own glory as they are. Challenges to self-serving behaviors are perceived as personal threats to their thin facade and any manner of defensive maneuvers will be employed in an effort to preserve their image and reputation. It is a universal truth that no one, in any endeavor, trusts or respects leaders who hold themselves to a lower standard of personal or professional conduct than they apply to others, or those who take full credit for the successes for which they were only partially responsible.

Leaders who are driven by an *Emphasis on Position* demand the full acclaim that goes with the title and position and as such, being in command becomes all about that which advances their own prestige. Any consideration of the needs and welfare of those under their authority is weighed against how their own interests may be served in the process of acting on behalf of another. Actions they consider that may benefit others must also provide some measurable benefit to them. If the manner in which you exercise your command authority emanates from a desire to serve your own image and reputation, you are choosing to sacrifice the loyalty and respect of your crew and flight decks commanded by such captains are operationally handicapped. In these instances, your leadership will be defined by a level of isolation from those with whom you are engaged in the accomplishment of shared goals. This is because when it becomes evident that the boss has no one's back but his own, what motivation is there for others to put forth more than the minimum required effort on behalf of the team? If the boss isn't going to look out for me, I have to look out for myself. If my actions also help the team I consider it a happy coincidence.

Leaders who are overly influenced by an *Emphasis on Position* believe that their status and reputation are the most important variables in every equation, and they tend to view other people as nameless members of the show whose role is to enhance the appearance and appeal of the star that is them. As with those overly influenced by an *Emphasis on Performance*, these individuals are often socially obtuse and lack awareness of the emotional dead and wounded left in the wake of their own vanity. For such individuals, looking good and being recognized as the biggest dog on the team is the guiding principle of leadership. At its core, an *Emphasis on Position* creates selfish leadership. Its single-minded devotion to the interests of the person with authority has a corrosive influence on the performance and morale of the team.

> For those given to an overdeveloped *Emphasis on Position,* authority and power are instruments of self-service.

When leaders with an over-developed *Emphasis on Position* look in the mirror, they see a king or a queen. People given to a self-image of "command royalty" tend to treat those under their authority as props whose primary function is to ensure that the royal name is the biggest and most prominent. Captains wear four stripes on their shoulders and on their sleeves, and not a crown.

Emphasis on Popularity – *"It's all about being liked."*

Within the realm of interpersonal relationships, there lives in the heart of every human a desire to be loved and respected by others. For some, this need is stronger than in others, and to the extent this is the primary factor that shapes and governs your exercise of authority your effectiveness as a leader will be neutralized. Leadership is not friendship, and I would strongly caution against allowing your *Attitude of Command* to permit the development of personal lenses that will blur your judgment and undermine your effectiveness. The primary role of the captain is to ensure that the flight is conducted in a manner that is safe, legal, and reliable. Period. If in the course of this pursuit those under your command determine that they like you, that's great. This is a bonus and should never be the primary desire that governs your leadership style. You need those under your authority to trust and respect you more than you need for them to like you.

Command is a big responsibility that often necessitates actions and decisions that may be unpopular with those under your command. Get used to it. Command can be lonely at times, and in order to be effective you must be willing to risk being unpopular. To the extent this is a consequence you can't abide your effectiveness as a leader will be nonexistent.

> Command can be lonely, and in order to be effective in your role as PIC you must be willing to deal with being unpopular.

When your decisions are framed by the degree to which they will either earn or forfeit the approval of others you are abdicating your command authority to them. Allowing the opinions of others to be the primary influence that governs your leadership is the act of surrendering your stripes. You have exchanged your position as Pilot In Command of a crew to that of Pilot Under Command. While generally acknowledged as the legal and official authority, your need to please will come at the cost of the trust and respect of your crew. A proper *Attitude of Command* requires the strength of character to maintain your resolve in the face of criticism and can make no allowance for the disapproval of others as the primary influence in your decision-making.

> Captains with a proper *Attitude of Command look forward* with confidence and conviction. Those motivated by a desire for popularity *look around* for guidance and direction. No one will be inspired to follow a captain who looks around more than they look forward.

Captains who include friendship on their list of the traits and skills of a leader lack the ability to see personal and professional circumstances with the clarity necessary to make tough decisions and will lack the resolve to initiate necessary but unpleasant conversations. As such, to the extent your leadership is characterized by a need for the approval of others, you will be tempted to pursue courses of actions that are motivated by a need for their endorsement and validation. By allowing approval to become a component of your leadership template, you are engaging in a practice of second-guessing your own decisions.

In these instances, indecision will characterize the manner in which you deal with conflict and operational challenges, and no one is motivated to follow the lead of a captain who has no confidence in their own judgment and is unwilling to risk the displeasure of others. Such is the action of one who lacks the fortitude necessary to lead, and this character flaw cannot be hidden from your crew. An *Attitude of Command* characterized by the need for approval will result in leadership that is indecisive. When this happens the trust of the crew will give way to disrespect.

> Members of a crew do not respect a captain whose primary goal is to be liked. Leadership is not friendship, and any attempt to achieve both will ultimately result in neither.

When leaders with an overdeveloped *Emphasis on Popularity* look in the mirror, they see a chameleon. Chameleons have an innate ability to change their colors in order to adapt to their surroundings. As such, they are reactive in nature, always looking for the safety afforded by blending in. For those with an overdeveloped need to be liked, the need for the approval will become the foundation for leadership that is reactive rather than proactive. The quest for popularity transfers command authority to those whose validation you seek and persuades you to surrender your stripes to those who don't yet wear them.

Here are some self-awareness reminders of the traits and

characteristics of captains who demonstrate the proper attitude of command. Each item on this list is meant to reinforce the principles defined by the leadership spokes by offering reminders of the cues and signals those under your command will look for as they assess and evaluate your credibility. Credibility is a crucial component of your effectiveness as a captain and will greatly influence the confidence your crew will have in your ability to lead them, and their belief in your commitment to their welfare. This kind of self-awareness is the beginning of leadership, just as the alphabet is the beginning of the process of learning to read.

1. Lead by example. *Learn to live the sermon you are preaching.* Leading by example means that you refuse to exempt yourself from the standards of performance or conduct that you apply to those under your command. Leaders must live by the norms they apply to others, and few things erode your credibility more than being a leader with two standards of conduct. Hypocrisy is a character flaw that squanders the trust and respect of others in a way that is swift and enduring.

I remember the first time I heard the term "two-faced" as a way of referencing the character and conduct of another person. Though the phrase is commonly used to describe someone who is disingenuous and insincere, I would also apply it to those in positions of authority who insist that others abide by standards to which they are willing grant themselves exemptions. When this happens, credibility gives way to resentment, and the only unity that exists within the organization is that enjoyed by those bound by their common bond of contempt for the boss with two faces. Lead with one face and not two.

Leading by example also means that your appearance and personal conduct reflect positively on yourself and the profession in that they indicate a sense of pride and self-respect. No one respects a leader who demonstrates little respect for themselves, and no one respects someone who holds themselves to a different standard than they apply to others. Why should others respect your rules and requirements when you don't?

- Be a leader worthy of the respect of your crew. **Look like a captain.**
- Be a leader others will want to emulate. **Act like a captain.**
- Be like the leader who made you want to be like them. **Inspire others to be a captain.**

> Refuse to hold yourself to a different standard of performance and conduct than you hold others. Lead with one face and not two.

2. Keep others in your loop. *Learn to think out loud.* The dynamics of the flight deck flow with greater ease and effectiveness when the captain thinks out loud with regard to the operation and the need for adjustments to the game plan. Crew effectiveness is enhanced when captains purpose to keep the crew apprised of their thoughts, concerns, and potential adjustments to the game plan. This deliberate action on the part of the captain serves to construct an accurate and shared mental model among the crew that results in enhanced Crew SA and an added margin of safety. Making decisions or adjustments to the flight plan without letting your crew in on your relevant thought processes is counterproductive to the operation. Let those under your command know what you are thinking and ensure they have an accurate sense of what direction you are taking them. Flight safety is never served and leadership is not being exercised appropriately when the captain expects the crew to be mind readers. Surprises are nice on birthdays, but they are never welcome on the flight deck.

> Don't expect those under your command to be mind readers.

3. Be adaptable. *Learn to expect and embrace the jazz.* The best leaders are those who are skilled at balancing symphony and jazz, i.e., structure and flexibility. Both are staples of the aviation playlist and competence with regard to your ability to hold them in balance will be required to varying degrees on every flight. The introduction of operational jazz to the structural symphony of flight planning can bring elevated levels of stress to the dynamics of the flight deck, and it is in those instances that a captain must be able to demonstrate composure under pressure.

The tone for the crew's ability to adapt to new and unforeseen situations is set by the captain, and the attitude that emanates from the left seat in the course of having to revise plans and expectations is echoed by the crew. While having a structured plan is important and necessary in aviation, a captain and a crew must be able to adjust to the new realities are introduced by unexpected operational developments. To the extent you lack the capacity to adapt to new circumstances and allow their introduction to create an attitude of operational pessimism you are undermining your effectiveness as a leader.

- Be structured. Be adaptable. Success requires both.
- Be confident under pressure. Steady hands are needed when the seas are choppy.

> The best captains are skilled in both symphony and jazz.

4. Be real. *Know how to say, "I don't know."* Being in command does not confer omniscience, and such an unrealistic expectation is usually self-imposed. Many have the opinion that reaching the left seat represents the culmination of your career aspirations, and for that reason, they are given to the belief that a captain must demonstrate mastery over all that can be known. If this is your conviction, let me be the first to pop your bubble. Becoming a captain is as much a beginning as it is a fulfillment of your career aspirations, and the truth is that you are just now embarking on the process of learning what it takes to realize your full potential as a professional aviator. While years of training and experience in preparation for assuming the responsibility of command have equipped you with the tools necessary for success, it is important not to allow yourself to believe that leadership means you are required to know everything, all the time. Such a belief is self-defeating, and to the extent you embrace it, you are faking it. Captains who fake it are taking the first steps to becoming *dangerously good.*

One of the lessons of experience is discovering that the gap between what you know and what you think you know is bigger than you ever imagined and that being a captain seems a whole lot easier when you are watching someone else do it. Given this reality, it is foolhardy to present and conduct yourself as one who by virtue of the additional stripe on their shoulder has gained access to all available knowledge. Don't let your stripes get in the way of your willingness to ask the necessary questions about the things you don't understand, and don't be afraid to download the knowledge and experience of those under your command.

- Be able to say, *"I don't know."* It humanizes you. People like human leaders.
- Believe in those under your command. Trust them to do their jobs.
- Be willing to own your mistakes. Surrender the facade of perfection.

> No one is fooled when you pretend to know things that you don't. Faking it undermines your credibility and the confidence of those under your command.

5. Be mindful of your shadow. *Understand the influence you have over others.* As a captain, you are always communicating with your crew—even when no words are being spoken. It is the nature of people to study those in positions of leadership. Never lose sight of the fact that factors such as your behavior, communication style, and the manner in which you respond to challenges and difficulties will influence the attitudes and performance of your crew. The captain has a greater degree of visibility than anyone else involved in the operation. Those under your command will study your posture and demeanor as you respond to challenges and will make mental notes about how and when to approach you with critical information. They will also decide whether they will want to be just like you some day or just the opposite. Those under you command will also pay close attention to your words, even when you don't give much thought to what you say.

The truth of this particular point was driven home one day as I chatted with my FO during our preflight briefing. We had flown together before, and I remembered him to be a top-notch aviator. At one point in our exchange, he said something that caught my attention. *"The last time we flew together was about a year ago, and on that trip you said something to me that I've never forgotten,"* were the words he used to recount a conversation that I had long forgotten but he had not. In fact, as he recounted the memorable words, it became clear that they had been etched into his psyche. I was gratified to learn that I had said something that he had found useful. The more I thought about this revelation of the positive impact I had made on another person with words that I didn't even recall, the more I began to wonder how often the reverse may be true and how many times I had said things that made an equally indelible impression in a negative way. I have no doubt that this is the case, and it was at about that time I heard a pastor make reference to this phenomenon when he said something along these lines. *"Every one of us has that person who we simply can't stand. Sometimes it's just because their nature and ours are different, but in many instances, these deep feelings are rooted in something that person said or did to you at some point that you just can't get over."* His summary really stuck with me. *"If you live long enough and especially if you serve in a leadership role, the chances are very good that there is someone out there for whom when they are asked to identify that one person that they just can't stand, their answer is YOU."* I didn't want to believe this at first because, like most people, I didn't want to consider the possibility that such a thing was possible. (Never underestimate the human capacity for self-deception.) Like most, I defaulted to a self-perception of one who is always considerate, engaging, and respectful to such a degree that I could not be capable of such insensitivities, but the more I thought about the pastor's words the more I became convinced of their truthfulness. We all have the capacity to exercise influence over others as a result of our words and actions and this is especially the case when you are in a position of leadership.

My conversation with the FO and the words of a sermon prompted me to reflect on the degree to which others can be influenced either positively or negatively by the things we say to them or perhaps in their presence. It was as a result of these two occasions that I became more committed to choosing my words with care and precision and recognizing and owning the instances in which I failed to do so. And, yes, I accepted the reality that there were most likely people out there for whom I was "THAT" person because of my poor choice of words and/or the manner in which they were delivered.

> The words of the captain have great capacity to influence the attitudes and performance of the crew. Words are like toothpaste in that once out of the tube, they are almost impossible to retrieve. Squeeze your words with care.

Proactive Flying

Remember that as a captain you are always on display and subject to the scrutiny of your subordinates. The words you use and the manner with which you deliver them have a great capacity to inflict lasting damage or encouragement. Be ever mindful of the importance of engaging others with tact, respect, and solid interpersonal skills, and understand how these factors work together to determine the operational climate of your flight deck.

This same admonition doesn't just apply to those in command. In the captain's absence, captains-in-training also have the capacity to exert a similar degree of influence over the support personnel with whom they engage. Endeavor to be intentional about treating each member of the team with dignity and demonstrating genuine respect for their contribution to the operation. This is part of your preparation for the addition of your fourth stripe.

> Those around you are influenced and impacted by your attitudes, decisions, and behaviors. This is especially true of the captain. Be mindful of this fact and conduct yourself with wisdom and prudence.

- Be self-aware. Choose your words with precision.
- Be socially aware. Pay attention to the impact of what you do and say.
- Be aware that you are on display. Consider the character qualities you are advertising.

Chapter 6

Be Crew Oriented

Know How to Build and Lead a Team

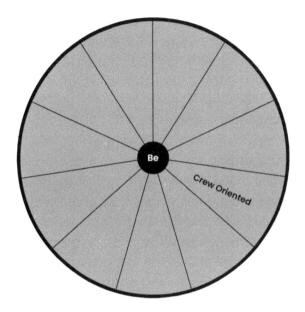

The interaction that takes place between a captain and the FO during their initial meeting as a crew establishes a foundation that will greatly influence their effectiveness as an operational team. This exchange between a captain and crew represents the transition from normal life to a process of focused attention and represents a critical opportunity for team building and the establishment of the manner in which command authority will be exercised on the flight deck.

Each member of the high-performance team that is a flight crew brings certain expectations to this critical first encounter and uses them as a baseline from which to get a sense of what to anticipate going forward. Captains tend to look for cues regarding the first officer's motivation and technical proficiency, while first officers are interested in discerning what it will be like to serve under this captain's leadership. These simultaneous evaluations are not unique to aviation and are common to the developmental phases of all interpersonal relationships. We all make similar evaluations when we first meet someone with whom we are going to interact on a personal or professional basis. The primary difference between these assessments and those involving flight crews has to do with the demands and complexity associated with flying and the degree to which flight safety is dependent upon the crew's ability to work together in a productive and effective manner.

Much has been said over the years about the importance of making a good first impression, and this truth certainly applies with regard to the initial meeting of a captain and a first officer. Before any words have been spoken, each individual has begun to take inventory of specific items on their mental checklist that give them an initial sense of what they can expect on the flight. Your first impression begins when the other person first sees you and not when you begin to speak. Your appearance, demeanor, and overall composure convey strong signals that create a solid impression that has already taken root in their mind before you even say hello. People tend to become attached to their first impressions of others, and these perceptions are often difficult to overcome even in the face of new information that contradicts their initial assessment. In point of fact, our first impressions are generally very accurate predictors of what we will experience in our working relationships with the other person.

When teaching on this subject, I would ask my students how long it would take them to formulate a sense of what it would be like to work for or with the other person. Although the answers given varied from *"almost immediately"* to *"a couple of minutes or so,"* the very consistent theme of their responses was that it didn't take long to construct a mental image of the pending dynamics for this flight. Immediately after that exchange, I would ask them to tell me how often their predictions materialized into reality. In other words, how reliable were your first impressions when it came to constructing your expectations for the flight? Again, there was an impressive degree of consistency in their answers, and the general theme of their responses can be summarized in two words—*"almost always."* When I asked them to share the specific evaluative tools they use when making their initial assessments, their responses fell into these general categories: appearance, demeanor, and confidence. While some may call these assessment criteria harsh, biased, and unscientific, the simple human truth is that even the most enlightened among us will employ these same factors to formulate an initial assessment of another person. Let's look at each of these evaluation criteria in some detail.

Appearance—How you look. This is an evaluation metric that has less to do with beauty and attraction than it does with the attention you give to your personal grooming and the manner in which present yourself. Looking like you slept in your uniform or presenting yourself as someone who has little regard for their personal fitness is perceived by many as an indication of a lack of self-respect. The immediate conclusion is, *"How can I respect someone who has no respect for themselves?"* Be attentive to your appearance, grooming, and overall level of fitness. All three reflect positively or negatively on the impression you make on others and is something we all know innately but often disregard. Lest there be any doubt about our intuitive understanding of the important role our personal appearance plays in making a positive impression, think back to the amount of time and effort you invested in preparing yourself for your most recent job interview or your first date with someone. In these high-stakes encounters you wanted to look your best and understood the importance of presenting yourself as someone who was both appealing and worthy of serious consideration. These are unique and infrequent events, and during subsequent encounters with the same people your attention to the details associated with your appearance would gradually relax. Anyone who has been in a long-term personal or professional relationship will attest to the gradual and progressive ease with which this relaxation of our standards can occur. It has been said that familiarity breeds contempt, and I would also add that in the context of personal appearance, it can also breed a degree of personal indifference and complacency that undermines your legitimate claim to the respect afforded to a professional. Indifference to your professional appearance is a common practice of the *dangerously good*.

> Getting others to respect you is difficult when you don't respect yourself. If you want to be perceived as a professional you must endeavor to look the part.

Demeanor—How you engage. While the goal of team building is not the development of friendship, there is much to be said about the importance of positive social and interactive dynamics among the crew. It's simply a fact that people tend to perform at a higher level and derive a greater degree of job satisfaction when they work in an environment that encourages interaction and mutual respect. Nothing fosters the creation of such an operational climate like the presence of a positive attitude, a willingness to engage openly and freely with the other, and a high level of motivation by both parties. To the extent you present yourself as someone who is irascible, negative, and unapproachable, you are sending strong signals of your unwillingness or inability to work closely and effectively with others.

In my years of teaching CRM, the hardest nuts to crack with regard to this factor were those I referred to as the "socially obtuse." These were the people whose internal wiring was not aligned with the common circuitry of social interaction. It is said of some people that "they don't get it," and when describing those who meet the definition of being grouped among the socially obtuse, it can be said that "they don't get that they don't get it." The socially obtuse, for whatever reason, lack the capacity to interact with others in a meaningful way or consider the degree to which their own words and deeds influence and impact those around them. They generally go through life unaware of the trail of emotional dead and wounded they have left in their wake. It is often the case that these individuals who lack the ability to interact with others in a meaningful and productive way are at the same time very accomplished in the technical aspects of the job, and it is my conclusion that they are far more comfortable in the company of things than the company of people.

Understand the importance of your social IQ as a factor in the creation of this first impression, and endeavor to make eye contact with the other person, offer a firm handshake, use and remember first names. In short, endeavor to treat them with the courtesy and respect they are owed and not simply as someone who is fulfilling an assigned role. Treat other people like they matter rather than as props on the stage for which you are the star attraction.

> Treat other people like they matter. This engenders respect and trust—both of which are essential to the creation of an effective team.

Confidence—How you carry yourself. In a general sense, people are drawn to those who exhibit a sense of confidence in themselves and in their ability to handle challenging situations. This is especially the case in a demanding and high-tempo profession like aviation. The people with whom you fly want a measure of assurance that the person strapped in beside them can withstand the demands associated with the job and won't fold under pressure. Confidence, or a lack thereof, is on display immediately as a function of your body language, and the first and strongest indication comes from your posture. Confident people engage the world with their heads up and their shoulders back and in that process signal their readiness to engage the task ahead with the conviction of one who is fully prepared to deal with whatever comes their way. Confidence is also demonstrated in the manner in which you approach the details of the task at hand, and your cards will be on display as you begin your discussion of the specifics of the flight. To the extent your response to the presence of bad weather at your destination or an inoperative system on your aircraft is flavored with the language of doubt or indecision you are signaling a lack of confidence in your ability to meet the challenge. A doom-and-gloom response of someone who embraces defeat before the game ever begins is not someone in whom I have a high degree of confidence. If you don't have confidence in yourself or your ability to meet the challenges ahead, how can you expect others to have confidence in you?

I am not recommending that you respond to the presence of threats to safety with false bravado in order to present a facade of confidence that you don't feel. This thin layer of armor fools no one and erodes the confidence others have not only in your ability but also in your sincerity. To the extent you will deceive yourself, you will distance yourself from others and lose their trust in the process. Don't let the heat melt your resolve, but instead, let it strengthen your commitment to meet the challenges ahead with conviction and confidence in your abilities.

Confidence is not only personal but also mutual and interactive. Each member of the flight deck crew must demonstrate confidence in the knowledge and skill of the other. Confidence is a force multiplier on the flight deck. Crews will have greater confidence in captains who have confidence in themselves. Furthermore, captains who demonstrate confidence in their crews by not micro-managing their efforts will be the recipients of enthusiastic support. Placing confidence in those under your command is easier when they have demonstrated initiative and competence. You want the captain to have confidence that you know what you are doing? You must first earn this trust by demonstrating initiative and competency. While this principle doesn't apply in every situation and there will always be those who micromanage others, as a general rule the confidence of the captain that affords you the respect of being trusted to do your job without constant supervision must be earned. This is not to say that a captain should not supervise and oversee the work of the crew, but it is meant to emphasize the need for a timely and appropriate approach to offering guidance or instruction. This is a balancing act that requires discretion and discernment on the part of the captain.

Proactive leadership allows others the latitude to employ their skills and resists the temptation to impede their efforts by offering too much in the way of guidance and instruction along the way. Unless and until those under your command give you a reason to doubt their knowledge, skills, and abilities, afford them the respect due to another professional and allow them the freedom to do their jobs without fear of the meddling voice of micromanagement.

A greater burden of responsibility and awareness for presenting these three traits in a positive manner rests on the shoulders of the captain. To whom much is given, much is expected, and it is the captain's appearance, demeanor, and confidence that set the tone for the creation of the operational climate of the flight deck. Captains must maintain a high level of awareness with regard to the standard to which they are held, and with regard to this initial encounter with an FO, let me say that for better or worse your reputation shows up well in advance of your arrival on the scene. Word gets out with regard to the nature and quality of the leadership demonstrated by every captain, and you can bet that the FO is comparing your actions with expectations derived from the feedback of those who have gone before you. One of the first questions in any conversation about an upcoming flight or evaluation is, *"Who are you flying with?"* This question is often a solicitation for information that provides insight about what to expect during your interactions with this individual, and as a result of what you are told by others it is possible to bring certain biases or assumptions to the first meeting that may be invalid. While the feedback of others can be helpful, let me caution you not to place too much reliance on someone else's assessment over your own judgment and experience. The fact that someone else had a bad experience with a particular crew member doesn't automatically mean that yours will be the same.

I remember learning this lesson during my days as a junior first officer. I was scheduled to fly with a captain who had a reputation of eating first officers for lunch. I listened to the stories of friends who had flown with this individual and laughed at their offers of last rites, and will confess to being nervous as I looked forward to the experience of flying with this captain. I remember showing up an hour before our scheduled show time and checking, rechecking, and double rechecking every aspect of the flight plan, weather, winds aloft, and Aircraft Maintenance Logbook (AML). I was determined not to be on this captain's menu and saw it as a challenge that would test my mettle. Some had encouraged me to call in sick and avoid the situation altogether, but that didn't strike me as a particularly courageous or professional course of action.

The fateful moment of our first meeting arrived, and the knot in my stomach tightened as the captain's shadow began to darken the flight plan as I studied it for the fiftieth time. The executioner was here, and as I turned to greet him, the tension between what I expected and what I experienced began to tighten. He was older and grumpier in appearance and demeanor than I had expected, had a frowning face that was not given to expressions of emotion of any sort, and his communication style was that of one who was a true believer in word economy. By that I mean he was one who believed in using the fewest number of words possible in any interpersonal engagement. His preferred method of communication was quickly established as "I ask simple questions to which I expect prompt and accurate responses." I never considered engaging in the customary banter that characterized my interactions with other captains and embraced his commitment to word economy. This felt more like a job interview than an attempt at team formation, and I knew that I had a good chance of getting hired as his hard edge softened with my ready responses to his detailed inquiries about the weather at our destination, applicable NOTAMS, and the maintenance history of the aircraft. He seemed satisfied and at times almost impressed by the fact that I had taken the time to do my homework. This set a tone that continued throughout our multiple-leg trip together, and I made it my mission to anticipate his questions and take the initiative to stay ahead of the flight plan. After a couple of legs of this, I sensed we had passed a significant milestone when he turned to me during the en route portion of our third leg to ask my opinion about which way we should deviate around a line of thunderstorms. I offered my recommendation and supporting evidence to make my case and to my surprise, he responded by saying, *"I agree. Tell ATC that's what we want to do."* My hunch was right. I had passed the interview and earned his confidence. I had made the team.

We flew together a number of times after that, and on each occasion I was intentional with regard to my level of preparation, initiative, and motivation to be the best possible first officer I could be. Over time the grumpy facade melted, and our relationship slowly developed into one that included meeting for dinner on layovers—something that was never sought or desired by those with whom he flew. I won't say we became fast friends, but we had achieved a level of mutual confidence in one another that led to the creation of a professional relationship that was characterized by trust and respect. We worked well as a team, and I even got him to laugh a couple of times. No one believed it, but it actually happened.

In time he shared his frustration with having to "babysit" first officers who showed up unprepared and lacking in the motivation or initiative necessary to earn his confidence. As he recounted situations and events that were the source of this frustration, I came to understand his perspective and came to see that his reputation as a captain who ate first officers for lunch was based in large part on the experience of those whose lack of proficiency and preparation made them menu items.

My point in sharing this story is to encourage you to do your part to earn the confidence of captains you fly with and resist the temptation to base your expectations of their leadership style solely on the testimonies of others. I'm not recommending that you discount any and all accounts from others altogether, but rather that you have confidence in your assessment and trust in your own judgment and experience in the formulation of your first impression. Don't be too quick to assume that someone else's story will be yours as well.

> When you meet a prospective crew member with whom you have not flown but have heard many stories, be inclined to give them the benefit of the doubt until they give you reason not to. Don't be too quick to conclude that someone else' story will be yours as well.

As a captain, you will be remembered more by your leadership than your stick-and-rudder skills. Few will remember what it was like to fly with you as the FO, but almost no one will forget what it was like to fly with you as a captain. They may not remember a lot about your proficiency as an aviator but are unlikely to forget what it was like to work for you and how you treated them.

> Your first impression doesn't begin when you start talking but when the other person first sees you. First impressions are lasting, and negative ones are difficult to overcome.

A critical ingredient regarding the first impressions between a captain and the FO is that of expectations. Each individual comes to this situation with specific expectations regarding the things they want to see from the other in order to give them a sense of what it will be like to work *with* or *for* the other person. The issue of the expectations that each member of the flight crew brings to the process of forming an operational team has been explored and studied in some detail over the years, and thousands of airline pilots in the US have been surveyed on the subject of what cues they look for during this first encounter that give them a measure of assurance or concern regarding the readiness, competence, and leadership of the person who will sit next to them on the flight deck. In these surveys, captains were asked to identify their expectations of first officers, and first officers were likewise questioned about what they expect of the captains with whom they will fly for the first time. In essence, they were asked to provide feedback regarding the specific cues or signals they look for when they meet their fellow crew member for the first time and begin the process of making an initial assessment as to whether that person is an operational asset or a liability.

Here is a list of the primary categories given by each seat position when asked what they look for in the other member of the crew. The items listed under one seat position reflect the expectations of the person in the other seat. For example, the items listed under "captain" reflect the expectations of the FO, and vice versa.

Captain

- **Leadership—**This is of primary importance to first officers as they assess a captain for the first time. First officers want to be assured that the captain is organized and thorough and that they will exercise command authority in a manner that welcomes participation from the crew. Being organized and thorough means demonstrating focused attention on important details and a vision for the conduct of the flight. If the first officer gets the sense that their captain is an authoritarian who only wants to give orders their assessment will likely be that communication on the flight deck will be monologues rather than dialogues.

  - Is this captain interested in my input, or will our communication be mostly one-directional?

- **Team formation—**Expectations regarding the nature of the captain's leadership are assessed not only as a function of their demeanor, approachability, and communication style, but also by the method by which they build their team. The process by which the captain establishes the working relationship on the flight deck establishes the climate of command on the flight deck. A healthy and productive operational climate is one in which open communication is encouraged. This, in turn, results in a healthy level of Crew SA that fosters sound operational decisions. The team building process greatly influences the crew's proficiency in dealing with threats to safety and to the extent the operational climate inhibits interactive communication, the crew is at greater risk for misfortune. The two primary ingredients of the team building process are setting the proper tone and defining expectations, and these components are discussed in greater detail below.

- Does this captain's team building establish an operational climate that facilitates the free and open exchange of information?

- **Initial briefings**—The quality of the initial briefing is critical to setting the operational tone for the flight. The two aspects of this initial briefing that are of critical importance to the FO have to do with technical competence and approachability. In the first instance, the FO will have more confidence in a captain who is command of their facts and establishes a clear plan for how the flight will be conducted. With regard to the second point, the FO is looking for cues as to whether the captain will be approachable and receptive to input. It has been shown that an FO is far more likely to speak up when they have been given a specific invitation by the captain to do so. This is especially the case in situations in which a young and junior FO is paired with an older and senior captain.

  - Do the captain's briefings convey a sense of competence, vision, and organization with regard to the technical aspects of the operation? Does the captain's initial briefing inspire confidence and trust?

- **SOP compliance**—Though this practice is generally assumed among professional aviators there is great value in having a captain verbalize a commitment to SOP compliance during the initial briefing with a new FO. This pledge provides a measure of certainty and reassurance that things will proceed as expected, and builds the FO's confidence in the captain.

  - Does the captain verbalize the requirement to operate the flight in accordance with SOP?

A captain's credibility as an effective leader worthy of the trust and confidence of the crew can be firmly established or irreparably damaged during this initial encounter with their crew. A captain with no credibility loses the respect of the crew, and when this respect evaporates, so does the captain's effectiveness as a leader. In these instances, others follow their lead because they are required to do so and not because they are inspired to.

> A first officer looks for credibility during the first encounter with a captain. A captain with no credibility loses the respect of the FO, and crew effectiveness is a casualty.

First Officer

Technical proficiency—Among the primary concerns on the mind of a captain regarding a first-time flight with an FO is that of their ability to do the job. A captain often asks questions about such things as the flight plan, weather requirements, or operational restrictions imposed by an MEL item as a way of determining the FO's level of knowledge and proficiency. Notice also that technical proficiency isn't listed as a primary concern by an FO in their initial briefing with a captain. The reason is that the technical proficiency of the captain is initially assumed by the FO. Knowing that the authority to command is given only to those who demonstrate competence and proficiency at the completion of a rigorous course of training and evaluation, this is a reasonable assumption on the part of the FO. The FO's sense of the captain's level of technical competence will be reinforced or undermined during the conduct of the initial briefing.

- A question on the mind of the captain is this: "Do I have confidence that this FO will be an operational asset or someone who will require constant supervision?"

Attitude and motivation—As discussed earlier, the attitude and motivation you bring to a task greatly influence not only the quality of your performance but also that of the working relationship you experience with others. The combination of a positive attitude and a willingness to take initiative are qualities that captains very much want to see in the first officers who strap in next to them on the flight deck. At a very minimum, the FO should arrive at least thirty to forty-five minutes prior to the scheduled "show time" and use this opportunity to familiarize themselves with all aspects of the pending flight. Meeting an FO for the first time who has taken the time to develop a comprehensive level of understanding of the operational specifics of the flight gives the captain a measure of confidence that their FO is up to the challenge ahead.

- Did this FO show up fully rested and ready for the flight?

Technical competence, attitude, and motivation are of primary importance to captains as they assess a first officer's operational fitness. Want to earn the captain's confidence during the initial team formation and briefing event? Be prompt. Be prepared. Know your stuff. Think ahead—don't passively wait to be told what to do.

> Captains want to be convinced that a first-time FO is not only proficient at their job but also motivated to do it well. Captains want to lead their FO, and not hold their hand.

Having your crew work together as a team from the very beginning goes a long way toward effectively dealing with threats to flight safety. Good interpersonal skills combined with the creation of a *closed comm loop* (discussed in a subsequent chapter) helps ensure an open exchange of operational information—a critical component of detecting and managing error. In addition, effective briefings allow a captain to define operational expectations, clarify workload assignments, and identify potential threats to safety and how to manage them.

The critical importance of building a cohesive and effective team was underscored by the findings of a classic NTSB study in the 1990s of thirty-seven air carrier accidents in which it was discovered that 73 percent of the mishaps were "first day/first leg" events. In the majority of these accidents studied by the NTSB, the crew had never operated together prior to the mishap, and a further examination of the data reveals a deficiency in the team-formation process during the initial encounter of the members of the crew. As a result of these findings, the specific steps to forming a team in a manner that establishes a productive operational climate were developed and implemented by most airlines. While there was some variation among different organizations with regard to the order of the steps and the terminology used to describe their facilitation, there was solid agreement about the critical aspect of this component of emphasizing the importance of this process as a component of achieving the operational goal of flight safety.

A landmark study by the NTSB of airline accidents found that 73 percent occurred on the "first day/first leg." Failure to set a proper tone and define operational expectations can have disastrous results.

The ability to build an effective team is critical to establishing a crew's operational identity and effectiveness, and it is in this process that the seeds of synergy and cooperation can either be developed or inhibited. Here are six steps that are helpful to building an operational team that will be equipped and prepared to identify and manage threats to safety promptly and effectively. To the extent this outline characterizes your approach to the critical process of team formation, you are embracing a process that will prepare your crews to more effectively manage threats to safety. As stated earlier, these steps are grouped into two general categories, *setting the proper tone and defining expectations.*

Setting the Proper Tone

1. **Establish a proper climate of command.** This refers to the manner in which the captain engages on an interpersonal level and the degree to which interaction between the two establishes a working climate characterized by open engagement. Captains set the tone for how the dynamics of the crew develop and must possess the social skills necessary for the creation of a working environment in which those under their command feel the freedom to engage in discussions that impact the operation. Captains with a low social IQ, or those who exercise their authority in a manner that discourages input and participation from their crew will be handicapped in their ability to make sound decisions. The goal of team building is to establish a working relationship that enhances the ability to maximize flight safety and team effectiveness.

> *Leadership* is not *friendship*. These two *ships* need never sail in the same waters.

Here are some specific tools that facilitate the development of a sound and effective climate of command.

A. *Personal introductions.* The captain should initiate personal introductions that include a firm handshake, eye contact, and the use of first names. Your crew is more likely to bring critical items to your attention when they believe you are approachable and willing to listen to their input. This approachability on the part of the captain fosters open communication, which results in the enhanced situational awareness necessary for sound operational decisions. As a captain, you want the person flying with you to feel the freedom to bring potential threats to safety to your attention, and those captains who present themselves as approachable and engaging are more likely to have access to this type of information. Captains who make it known that they don't want or need input from those under their command are less likely to receive it.

> Captains who give the impression that they don't want or need input from those under their command are far less likely to receive it and this kind of leadership compromises safety.

B. Tone and body language. These are more reliable indicators of the true meaning of a person's communication than the words they use, and for this reason, it is important for the captain to pay attention to these aspects of their messaging. A dismissive tone or body language that conveys a sense of indifference or detachment will send a message that undermines your ability to build a cohesive team. As the saying goes, "You only get one chance to make a good first impression," and it is possible for your tone and body language to completely undermine the message you convey with your words.

2. Establish a pattern of closed loop communication. By asking simple questions with "knowable" answers, you are establishing a pattern of communication in which each question or comment solicits a response from the other party. This pattern is called *closed loop communication*, and it cultivates the practice of ensuring that the exchange of information is bi-directional. Questions about the upcoming flight, such as, "How does the weather look at the destination?" or "Have you looked at the MEL?" are questions for which there are easy answers, and this process affords the captain an opportunity to gauge the FO's level of motivation and preparation. Additionally, "getting to know you" questions, such as, "What's your background?" will facilitate the give and take of open communication. This practice will establish a pattern of interpersonal dynamics that will serve you well during the flight. To the extent this interactive process is established and reinforced in the low-stress environment of the briefing room, the chances of it being exercised in demanding, high-tempo situations are enhanced.

3. Establish experience levels. Questions about the FO's experience are meant to reinforce the closed loop while providing an operational backdrop that determines how you operate as a crew. This exchange is essential, as it is important to know something about the experience level of the person with whom you are about to go flying. *"How long have you been on the airplane?"* or *"Have you ever operated into this airport before?"* are essential bits of knowledge that will flavor the manner in which you brief and operate. Knowing that you are flying with someone who is new to the airplane may influence the manner in which the initial briefing is conducted. For example, when flying with someone who is new to the airplane or has never operated into the busy airport to which you are about to fly, you will probably spend more time briefing items that you may abbreviate when flying with someone who has more experience. If you as a captain are new to this particular aircraft or are operating to a particular destination for the first time, it is essential that you offer that information as well. It may be the case that the FO has more recency of experience than you, and you would do well to avail yourself of the benefits of their experience and local knowledge as you conduct your briefing.

4. Establish credibility. It is during the initial briefing that the captain demonstrates competence and a clear vision for the conduct of the flight. In short, the captain must outline the game plan in a manner that inspires operational trust.

Defining Expectations

5. Establish intentions. In addition to the interpersonal aspects of this first encounter, the captain must be clear with regard to operational expectations and *intentions* for the conduct of the flight. A statement by the PIC of the intention to operate in accordance with SOP is an operational contract of sorts between the captain and the crew and establishes a baseline of expectations that are mutually understood. This agreement establishes a framework of operational trust that fosters confidence about the task ahead. It is also important to understand that the operational benefits derived through the SOP contract can be quickly rendered null and void when a captain chooses to violate its terms for reasons of preference or convenience. When this happens, it may be impossible to restore the trust you once enjoyed, and in that moment you have chosen to introduce an unwanted threat to safety to take residence on your flight deck.

6. Establish requirements. It is also imperative that the captain make an explicit statement regarding the *requirement* of those under their command to speak up when they become aware of an operational concern that represents a present or potential threat to safety. A captain cannot assume the ability to be simultaneously aware of every aspect of the operation and must learn to depend on the input of the crew. In short, the captain's ability to make solid operational decisions is only as good as the quality and timeliness of the information at his or her disposal, and the crew must be actively engaged in providing that which the captain needs. The captain must not characterize this exchange as simply a desired component of the dynamics of the flight deck, but convey it as a requirement. Captains are most effective when they know what the crew knows during the operation of the flight. As stated earlier, research has shown that junior members of the crew are more likely to be proactive with their input and forthcoming with their operational concerns when such a requirement has been established by the captain.

These steps are essential to setting the proper tone for the flight and defining expectations with regard to how the aircraft will be operated. To the extent they are followed, there is a higher probability that the flight will be conducted within the boundaries of the Crew Envelope. The quality of the team formation process establishes a baseline of understanding that influences crew performance and will enhance or detract from flight safety for the duration of the flight.

LEADERSHIP

Chapter 7

Be Coach Oriented

Know How to Invest in Others

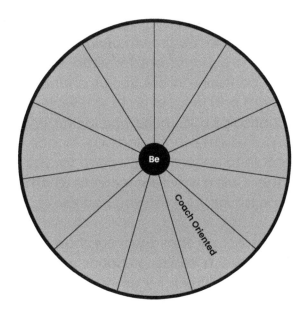

H

ave a Mentor. Be a Mentor.

With regard to the nature and exercise of leadership on the flight deck, there are two roles to consider. You are either a captain or a captain-in-training. Be mindful of this distinction, and during your time in the right seat, be focused on the fact that your time as an FO is meant to train and equip you with the attitude and skills necessary for your move to the left seat. Commit to learning from the captains with whom you fly by asking them questions about the way they dealt with a particular situation or the factors that entered into an operational decision. Find a captain you respect and whose leadership skills you admire, and ask for their feedback on how you dealt with situations of your own. As a captain-in-training, you must be curious and teachable, and when you become a captain, you must continue to be both. I recommend that everyone aspire to constantly be the middle portion of what I call a *"mentoring sandwich"* Mentoring is much like a sandwich in its structure and in the hierarchy of aviation there will always be people above you and others below in terms of experience. Make a point to be learning from someone who has been where you aspire to go at the same time you are investing in the growth of someone who is coming along behind you. It is important to establish and maintain a relationship with someone more senior and experienced who can impart wisdom and instruction to you while simultaneously cultivating relationships with those who lack your experience for whom you can provide the same kind of guidance. One need not be a senior captain to be a mentor, and regardless of your level of experience, there will always someone to whom you can offer instruction on the things you wish you had known back then.

The best mentors are those who embody the qualities of honesty, humility, and a sense of honor in addition to those outlined on the Crew Wheel. It has been my experience that one need not take out an ad requesting or offering to be a mentor (that would be weird), but instead let these relationships develop naturally and organically. You will be naturally drawn to those with whom you feel comfortable having these types of conversations, and the same is true of those who will seek your guidance.

It is my belief that mentoring relationships work best when they are informal and conversational rather than scheduled and regimented. The interpersonal give-and-take associated with mentoring is far more effective when it occurs in the context of an event or situation that provides a "teachable moment," rather than as prescribed in an outline or a curriculum. Mentoring is real-life instruction and as such should be conducted in the context of actual circumstances.

Let's take a closer look at the three important ingredients of a mentor: honesty, humility, and a sense of honor.

Honesty— Mentoring is best done by a coach rather than a cheerleader. A good coach has the insight, experience, and willingness to tell you the things you need to hear and offers them from the perspective of one who wants you to improve. Sometimes the coach will tell you things that cause you to bristle, but it's something they are willing to do because they know you need to hear them more than you may want to, and unpopularity is a price they are willing to pay on your behalf. Cheerleaders, on the other hand, only have the capacity to offer repetitive platitudes of hollow words that lack the power to influence your actions. In fact, you will become less inclined to listen to the cheerleader because you have come to understand that they only tell you that you are wonderful and that *"you can do it."* After a while you don't even hear them because you have learned not to believe them. No one is awesome all the time, no one deserves a trophy for every game. Cheerleaders may be heard, but it is the coach who is actually listened to when the game is on the line. Think about it this way. When it's fourth and goal and you call a timeout to discuss the play, whose recommendation do you covet most, the coach or the cheerleader?

> Find a mentor who is a coach and not a cheerleader. Strive to become that person for someone else. People may hear the cheerleaders, but they listen to the coach.

Humility—This ingredient refers to the willingness on the part of the mentor to be candid with regard to their own learning curves from days gone by. The most effective mentors are those who can balance the offer of instruction with the lessons learned from their own mistakes, and I've never been inclined to sit under the instruction of someone who presents themselves as infallible and thus incapable of relating to the situation in which you may now find yourself. For me, such individuals are impossible to relate to, and my encounters with them always made me come away wishing I had never engaged with them in the first place. Humility characterized by a willingness to tell on yourself humanizes the mentor and helps to make their lessons more relatable. The best mentors are those who know how to talk *with* others rather than *at* them. A personal mentor for whom I had tremendous respect was one whose style was to use the lessons learned from his own mistakes as teaching tools when it was appropriate. This isn't to suggest that his style was one of self-flagellation, as there is no element of self-respect in this method, but was instead one that recognized the wisdom of humanizing a personal experience in order to make a point. One of his favorite lines was the admonition to *"use me as a warning and not as an example"* as he prepared to offer an account of an important lesson he had learned. This person was honest not only when it came time to offer correction or recommendations to others, but also with regard to his own shortcomings and the things he had learned as a result of his missteps. He never held himself up to be one who was faultless and without blame, and his approach to mentoring was characterized by a balance of "what you need to do" instruction with that given from the perspective of "here's what you might think of next time, and "let me tell about a guy who found this out the hard way."

I still recall the things he taught me and the genuine manner with which they were shared. His humility made his lessons seem more meaningful and his commitment more authentic. He is someone for whom I could cite many occasions in which I could say, *"You told me something once that I'll never forget . . ."*

> Humility is an essential quality for a mentor. Fallible mentors are far more effective than those who attempt to project an image of perfection.

Honor—The inclusion of the word invest in the title of this chapter is meant to underscore the importance of committing yourself to something bigger than yourself. In this case, that something is the future growth and development of the profession and all who comprise its ranks. To some this may sound like an old-fashioned call to advocacy for an ideal, but for me it's pretty simple. People tend to pursue a profession like aviation because of their love of flying, and over time this devotion develops into a deep and abiding affection for everything you learned in the process of earning the right to wear wings on your uniform. Aviation is not just a job or a profession, but a unique way of life to which your love and commitment motivate a desire to ensure that its standards are preserved. There is a type of pride in what you have achieved that can only be understood and appreciated by those who ever engaged in the challenges that shaped your experience. This bond cultivated a desire to ensure that those who come behind you are not only prepared for what lies before them but also committed to "leaving the profession better than they found it."

The decision to invest in someone or something is underscored by our belief in its intrinsic value and potential. Mentoring is an investment in the future of the profession and those who will fill its seats and is motivated by a desire for both to flourish in equal measure. Find a mentor, and be a mentor whose genuine love of the profession motivates you to inspire others to the same level of desire. For such people, mentoring is not just a duty; it's an honor.

> The best mentors are those who aspire to leave the profession better than they found it.

A leader never stops being a mentor to those under their command, and every captain has a responsibility to mentor to those under their command. Consider each first officer with whom you fly to be a captain-in-training, and seize every opportunity to invest in their growth and, by extension, that of the industry you love. Who is better equipped to train the next generation of captains?

An excellent opportunity to engage in helpful conversations designed to guide and direct these future captains is available at the completion of every flight. After the engines have been shut down and the checklists are completed, take a few moments before you go your separate ways to conduct a debrief. There is always something that can be learned and, for the captain, this is the chance to offer insight, correction, and guidance. It's mentor time. I encourage every captain to engage in this process using a simple and interactive method that is based on three simple questions:

- What did we do well individually and as a crew?
- What could have been done better?
- Are there any lessons to take forward?

This process encourages a dialogue that will foster real-world learning and self-awareness. This debrief is an interactive process that invites opportunities for the captain to mentor the FO and also receive feedback that will advance his or her own professional growth. I remember a debrief with my FO after a stressful flight that included unexpected weather at our destination, holding, and a divert to our alternate. When I asked the FO for his assessment I was surprised to learn that my rapid-fire communication style during holding introduced an element of confusion at the worst possible time. So much for being Mr. CRM. His assessment was accurate and I needed to hear it. Had I not asked for his feedback I doubt that I would have had the opportunity to shine the light on a personal blind spot. As I recall this event I am reminded of the discussion in chapter 5 about the absence of feedback as one of the primary reasons for ineffective leadership. The debrief I just described reinforced my belief that captains who open the door for feedback will avail themselves to opportunities for personal growth.

While the ideal model for a debrief is interactive, there are times when an FO's experience level is such that a more direct approach would be more productive and appropriate. Sometimes the FO's lack of experience and awareness is such that the captain will deem it necessary and constructive to conduct the debrief in a more instructive manner. In either case, the goal is the same. The debrief must be motivated by a desire on the part of the captain to aid the junior members of the crew in their professional development and to be open to input regarding their own performance.

The best captains are those who remain teachable, and it is those captains who see themselves as having reached the point in their career of not needing to learn anything new who are themselves threats to safety. Experience is a wonderful teacher, and to the extent it has taught you to expect only successful outcomes, you have reached the point in your career where you are at risk of becoming *dangerously good.* As stated in a previous chapter, long periods of success can infuse us with a sense of invincibility that has the potential to influence our judgment to the point that we take unnecessary risks that result in poor operational decisions.

Those who aspire to become captains would do well to spend some time as a flight instructor. There is an old adage that says, "If you really want to learn something, teach it." I have certainly found this to be the case in my career, and looking back, I can attest to the fact that the amount of preparation required to prepare for each flight or simulator event with a student pushed me to pursue a mastery of procedures, aircraft systems, and rules and regs to a greater degree than at any other time in my career.

It is also the case that when you are serving in the role of instructor, you are essentially the captain of the training event. You are in command of the entire evolution from the brief to the debrief. As the instructor, you set the tone for the interaction between you and the student, and the manner in which you establish credibility and exercise authority greatly influence the student's ability to learn. The skills that make you a good captain in terms of your ability to understand the technical aspects of the job and also the nuances of motivating, correcting, and mentoring others are very much the same as those that make you a good instructor. As such, being a flight instructor is a leadership laboratory, as you are practicing and honing the same skills that will prepare you to command a crew.

This is a type of mentoring that is most effective when a particular pattern is followed. This pattern is outlined in the following four stages of instruction:

1. Trainer
2. Teacher
3. Coach
4. Peer

Let's examine each in some detail.

1. **Trainer.** *Tell them what to do.* In this phase you impart the skills and habit patterns necessary for their development. At this point of their training they lack sufficient knowledge to fully understand all the reasons why certain procedures and habits are important. Compare this to the methodology parents use with young children. In their younger years, kids are taught not to run out in the street or touch a hot stove. While lacking the ability to understand why these prohibitions and restrictions are necessary, they must learn to trust in the judgment and experience of their parents. Compliance with the instructions of their parents is in the child's best interests, and develops a solid foundation for the relationship.

   This phase fosters trust.

2. **Teacher.** *Tell them why* it is done this way. As your students gain both knowledge and experience, they are better equipped to understand the reasoning behind the instructions and restrictions they have been given. As a teacher, you are actively involved in the process of helping them discover the *why* that governs the dictates of the previous stage of instruction.

Using the example of raising children, it is only after they reach a certain age and level of cognitive development that they are able to understand the reasons that prompted the guidelines and restrictions they were given at an earlier age. Only now can they see the wisdom of what they were trained to do, and the learning becomes real to them, and retention is enhanced as rules and reasons become blended. Once a student trusts you to train them, they will want you to teach them.

This phase fosters learning.

3. **Coach.** *Guide them as they develop.* This stage comes when your student has developed a sufficient level of knowledge and skill to be able to operate more independently. In the case of student pilots, they have demonstrated the proficiency necessary to pass a check ride or fly their first solo cross-country. In these instances, your role shifts to one that is more focused on directing their development from afar. They have taken what you taught them and are now learning how to apply the lessons on their own. The trick for the coach is to know when to exercise restraint and when to step in to provide direct assistance. It has been my experience that lessons learned from my own mistakes are the ones that have paid the biggest dividends in terms of personal and professional growth. There is no hard-and-fast rule here, and while there is no useful purpose served by allowing

students to put themselves in unnecessary danger, there is real value in letting them make mistakes. The lessons they learn from the experience of failing are usually more memorable and helpful than twenty-five briefing room lectures about what to do and what to avoid.

This phase fosters confidence.

4. **Peer.** *Work alongside them.* At some point, your students will have reached a level of experience and proficiency that qualifies them to operate alongside you as a professional peer. There are fewer experiences more rewarding than flying with someone who was once your student and watching with a sense of pride as he or she manages both the aircraft and operational situations with poise and confidence. It's not unusual in the aviation industry to have the experience of flying with someone who was once your student. To the extent your professional relationship prior to this moment were in the context of these steps of the instructor-student relationship, the experience of operating together as fellow professionals will be very rewarding.

This phase fosters job satisfaction.

It is important that these steps be followed in the proper sequence. As an instructor, just as with a captain, your initial step must not be the cultivation of friendship or a peer relationship. Such a focus is misplaced and will erode the student's respect for your authority, and as a result the job of instruction and evaluation likely will become unnecessarily complicated to the point of dysfunction. Lest there be any doubt of the wisdom of this, think about people whose parenting style is characterized by a desire to be their child's friend rather than their parent. It is never a pretty sight to watch adults surrender their parenting stripes as they treat their young children like friends or peers and negotiate or bribe them in an effort to gain compliance. As with parenting, this must be the final stage of the student-instructor relationship, and to the extent the other steps were followed in their correct order, will be the most rewarding.

It has been my experience that the most effective mentors are also the most humble about their abilities and achievements, and this seems to be a common trait of exceptional people. They don't think that what their actions are exceptional, because in their minds, what they are doing is simply consistent with how things should be done. In fact, the exceptional are often the most forthcoming about their need for improvement, tend to shy away from accolades, and are more open to instruction. By contrast, the incompetent are typically far more given to overstating their abilities and achievements and lack the capacity to conduct an honest assessment of their own strengths and weaknesses. The incompetent are also less likely to seek or receive constructive criticism from a mentor, nor are they equipped to serve in this role. Their inputs are more likely to consist of one-directional sermons or overinflated recitations of their own glory days.

> The most accomplished are often the most humble, and when this combination is present in someone, you are looking at a prime candidate for a mentor. The best teachers are themselves the most teachable.

Your tenure as an instructor affords you the opportunity to work with all types of people, and this experience provides tremendous insight that will help you further quantify your own grasp of what it takes to be a good leader and a trusted mentor.

Mentoring others requires the presence of a strong commitment to the pursuit of excellence. Given that one cannot instruct others in the development of the skills and character qualities that they don't possess those mentors must hold themselves to the highest possible standards. No one wants to be mentored by someone whose own professional house is not in order. Anyone who aspires to be a mentor must reflect the qualities outlined by the spokes of the Crew Wheel.

Mentoring others is both a privilege and a responsibility. Remember that when you are in a leadership position you will be constantly studied by others. They look for reasons to trust in your example and are using you as the model from which to develop their own composite sketch of what a leader looks like. A captain is always mentoring through their actions and attitude and must always be mindful of the influence.

As a captain you must add an additional "M" to your underestimating of CRM and practice CRMM. Crew Resource Management and Mentoring. Mentor with your life and not just with your words. What you model has a greater impact and is a more reliable guide than what you say. A perfect reminder of the importance of this principle is found in the following quote by Benjamin Franklin: *"Well done is better than well said."*

> In order to be an effective mentor, you must first match the description of a professional.

Professional Aviator's Pledge

This pledge is a tool for assessing your level of commitment to the qualities and standards that describe the attitudes and behaviors of a professional. Much like the PAPI tool, it is offered as a means of self-assessment regarding the comparison between where you are and where you need to be. The elements of this pledge are comprised of a list of statements that outline and define what it means to be a professional aviator. While this pledge has broad application, in some instances it makes specific reference to instructors and captains. It is my hope that every aviator will be known by this pledge.

Professional Aviator's Pledge

- I will show up fully rested and prepared to brief, operate, and debrief every event to the best of my ability.

- I will brief and debrief each event fully and completely and find answers to questions to which I do not know the answer.

- I will actively scan for threats to safety and remind others to do the same.

- As an instructor or captain, I will not undermine the credibility of established policies and procedures in the presence of my students or my crew.

- I will stay current and up-to-date on the latest revisions and procedures.

- I will not intentionally violate SOP and will challenge those who do.

- I will endeavor to ensure that my appearance, demeanor, and conduct inspire trust and confidence among those over whom I have professional influence.

- I will be mindful of the fact that when I wear the uniform, I am an ambassador for the profession and will endeavor to represent it with pride and respect.

- As an instructor or evaluator, I will "call them as I see them" and not allow myself to be influenced by schedules, personal bias, or other factors as a metric for assigning a passing or failing grade.

- I will use my talents and skills to promote flight discipline and solid airmanship for as long as I am privileged to wear the uniform.

COMMUNICATION

Chapter 8

Be Engaging

Know the Fundamentals of Effective Communication

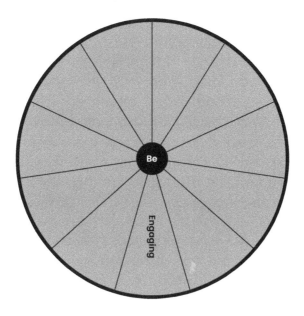

We Need to Talk

In this chapter, we will examine the basics of communication and the various factors that can conspire to make the process of understanding one another more difficult than necessary.

In the early days of accident investigations, the general term *pilot error* was often used to ascribe causality and blame in the aftermath of a mishap. At first glance, this term would suggest a lack of technical proficiency on the part of the crew as the primary causal factor, and blame for the accident was typically assigned to pilots who were simply not up to the challenge before them. As the process of analyzing the interpersonal dynamics on the flight decks of these accidents became more focused and sophisticated, it was discovered that the term *pilot error* was both simplistic and misplaced, and in truth, accidents most often occurred when the boundaries of the Crew Envelope were violated. Of primary interest to those engaged in the process of analyzing the causal factors of accidents was the frequency with which poor communication between the members of the crew or with ATC contributed to the commission of the preventable errors that resulted in tragedy. The link between effective communication and flight safety has since been well established and validated, and it is an undeniable fact that crews who communicate more effectively with one another and with ATC operate at higher levels of proficiency and enjoy greater margins of safety. Furthermore, it is undeniable that this connection between communication and flight safety begins with the operational climate established by the captain during the team formation process.

Captains whose communication styles are more top-down and one-directional rather than interactive run the risk of discouraging input from their crews and thus isolating themselves from potentially critical information. Exercising your authority with a heavy hand invites the opportunity for a threat to safety to sit on your jump seat.

Communication is essential to the creation of a *shared mental model,* which is a critical component of identifying and managing threats to safety. A *shared mental model* exists when every person involved in the operation has the same level of awareness regarding what is happening and what has happened and, based on those two factors, what *needs* to happen in the future. Flying is a dynamic process, and there must be a continuous level of shared awareness regarding all facets of the operation. To the extent that something that *has* happened goes unnoticed or is misinterpreted, the crew's understanding of what is *now* happening is fundamentally flawed, as will be their determination of what future actions *will be* taken. Misinterpreting an ATC clearance creates a present level of misunderstanding that will result in poor SA and flawed decisions.

> 70 percent of ASRS reports are related to communication issues.

The link between communication and SA is critical to flight safety and cannot be established when information is not shared equally and accurately. Mutual comprehension of operational data is essential and must be an ongoing component of the dynamics of the flight deck. To the extent critical knowledge is known and understood by only one person, the crew is operationally handicapped.

Comm 101

Let's begin our examination of communication with a look at the basic elements of human interaction. As this diagram suggests, communication looks simple enough when displayed in this format, but as we shall see, the opportunity for unnecessary complications and confusion is ever present.

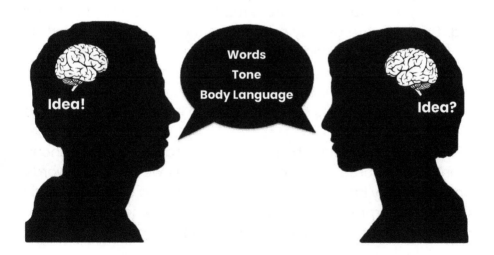

As the sender of a message, you have an idea that you want to convey to the *receiver* and will engage in a process of formulating and "encoding" it in such a way that ensures accuracy. This encoding process includes your choice of words, the tone with which they are delivered, and the conscious or unconscious addition of body language. All three work together to convey a message that is then "decoded" by the receiver as they attempt to decipher its true meaning. Based on their interpretation of the sender then engages in a similar process of encoding in order to formulate an appropriate response. Though this process of volleying ideas back and forth sounds easy enough there are plenty of factors that can cause clarity to be replaced with confusion.

When it comes to interpersonal communication, all of us are equipped with interpersonal decryption software that our brain uses to discern the true nature of the messages we receive. This software is a standard component of every person's operating system and serves as our personal interpreter. Each person's interpreter is always on duty as it analyzes the words, tone, and body language associated with incoming messages in an effort to identify the true and accurate meaning of what they are being told. This software usually operates without conscious effort on our part and is designed for the pursuit of accuracy.

Let's take a closer look at the three aspects of communication our software evaluates and compares in its quest for accuracy.

A classic study done by Dr. Albert Mehrabian of UCLA[1] shows an interesting breakdown of the emphasis we place on words, tone, and body language as we search for cues that will provide a reliable interpretation of the messages we receive. According to Dr. Mehrabian's research, words comprise only 7 percent of

---

[1] Mehrabian, A., & Wiener, M. (1967). Decoding of Inconsistent Communications. *Journal of Personality and Social Psychology*, 6(1), 109–114

our interpretation of a verbal message, the tone of voice used by the speaker conveys 38 percent of the its true meaning, and a reliance on the signals given by the body language of the speaker exerts the greatest influence on the listener's interpretation at 55 percent.

Words—*What You Say*

Words are certainly an important component of communication and is the area upon which people are most conscious and focused as they prepare to engage with others. Words have meaning, and it is critical that your verbal offerings be chosen with clarity and precision. As we shall see, the use of slang words or phrases can introduce ambiguity and confusion and for that reason careful attention must be given to *what* you say. Words are spoken thoughts, and of the three aspects of communication are the most likely to be voluntary and intentional. It is also interesting that of the three components of our decryption software, words exercise the smallest amount influence in the work of interpretation. While words certainly matter, the bigger truth is that our tone and body language matter more.

> Choose your words carefully, but be more careful that they are not contradicted by how you say them.

Tone—*How You Say It*

We are all familiar with the adage, *"It's not what you say; it's how you say it."* This truth underscores the point that the tone of voice used to deliver your chosen words can significantly alter their interpretation. This is especially the case when the tone that becomes their delivery vehicle is fueled by strong emotions or laced with sarcasm. If I were to say to you, *"I like your shoes,"* using an upbeat tone, chances are you would take this as a compliment. If, however, I spoke the exact same words with a tone that offered even the slightest hint of ridicule regarding your choice of footwear, chances are this would be interpreted quite differently. In each instance, the words were exactly the same, but the inclusion of a critical tone in the second instance would prompt a completely different response. Using the example of volleying ideas, this would be perceived as spiking the ball and would prompt a completely different response than the use of the same words offered with a positive delivery. response. Tone is not always a negative thing and can be used to emphasize a point when it is consistent with spoken words.

Tone can easily be used to weaponize conversations, and a negative tone can easily be perceived as a personal attack. A negative tone is a triggering mechanism that adds the dimension of unpleasant emotions into the volley, and interpersonal friction can ensue when the parties involved lack the maturity or discipline to recognize its harmful influence. The emotions that can erupt from the use of a derisive tone are likely to consume logic and reason and it is in these moments that people are most apt to say the things that they will live to regret. Words are like arrows, and once they have left the bow they can't be retrieved. As we shall see in our discussion of conflict resolution, tone must be corralled and managed when emotions are strong, and it for this reason that some conversations need to be deferred to a later time. Your decryption software analyzes and compares spoken words and the tone with which they were delivered, and as Dr. Mehrabian's findings suggest, when there is a discrepancy between the two, more credence is given to tone as a reliable indicator of the nature of the message. Tone can negate or significantly alter the meaning of our words, and during verbal volleys it is critical that our delivery style be given the same careful attention as our choice of words.

> Your tone can emphasize or negate the meaning of the words you speak, and for that reason you must strive to manage your delivery style with the same care given to your choice of words.

Body Language—ial *What You Show*

Body language is a topic that has gotten a good deal of press over the years, and by now many are familiar with its use in law enforcement interrogations. By definition, the term *body language* is a reference to the nonverbal cues and signals that are communicated by all humans through such methods as posture, facial expressions, hand gestures, and even the direction and movement of our feet during a conversation.

I became interested in the subject after reading a book called *What Every Body Is Saying*, written by a retired FBI agent named Joe Navarro. As I read his account of what he had learned about reading people during his years as an investigator, I was fascinated by the myriad of nuanced and subtle ways people communicate their true thoughts and feelings through nonverbal signals. While I never considered myself to be an expert on the subject, the things I learned from Agent Navarro's book taught me to better appreciate and discern the nonverbal cues being given by those with whom I engaged and to cultivate an awareness of how easily my nonverbal messages could contradict those conveyed by my words and tone.

> Your body is always communicating, even when no words are being spoken. Be mindful of the nonverbal messages you are sending, and know that your body speaks louder than your words and the tone with which they are delivered.

Body language is a critical part of the volley of communication and, as Dr. Mehrabian's research suggests, is arguably the loudest in that it exerts the greatest amount of influence in our software's assessment of the true meaning of an incoming message.

At a basic level, the brain's purpose for relying on nonverbal cues as its primary point of reference is to determine if the other individual is friendly or has the potential to cause harm. As such, this portion of your decryption software is programmed to act as early warning system. Interestingly, when the brain identifies a contradiction between the spoken words it *hears* and the nonverbal cues it *sees*, it will always defer to the latter for a true interpretation of the message or intentions of the sender. Your software is making assessments about the other person before they even speak, and for this reason, it is important to remember that the first impression you make on another person is being formulated before you even say hello.

> The first impression you make of another person is being formulated before you even say hello. Appearance, demeanor, and attitude are being scanned and analyzed by a person's decryption software well in advance of the first verbal exchange.

Be mindful that in the case of any disparity between the three modes of communication your brain is likely to rely on body language as the most reliable analytical tool. To the extent that you lack awareness regarding the influence of body language on the interpretation of your communication with others your ability to develop a shared mental model with your crew will be lacking.

In addition to the potential for confusion due to the mixed signals that are processed by our software there are additional elements that can impair our ability to communicate effectively.

While our decryption software is an internal filter, factors I refer to as *communication pollution* are largely external and multifaceted. By definition, *communication pollution* is any influence that can replace clarity with confusion in the exchange of ideas. The potential for pollution exists in every conversation and while it can result in difficulty or embarrassment in personal relationships, its presence on the flight deck can result in lost SA and poor decisions.

> A crew's ability to establish and maintain a shared mental model is undermined when clarity is polluted by the presence of confusion.

Here are some examples of factors that can introduce communication pollution:

1. *Slang.* I have a friend from England with whom I enjoy a good deal of friendly banter. We laugh a good deal about the differences in American and British words, especially our use of slang, and our conversations remind me of the quote by George Bernard Shaw that *"Britain and America are two nations separated by a common language."* This potential for misunderstanding also exists between people from different parts of our own country as we use regional slang. One of my roommates in the navy was from Boston and there were times when it felt like we needed an interpreter.

2. *Language differences.* Anyone who has spent time in a foreign country can attest to the difficulties associated with trying to communicate with people whose native tongue is different from your own. It's interesting to watch as body language and loud repetition are employed in an effort to remedy such a communication impasse, and

it's often the case that we end up pointing to pictures of things we both recognize or engage in an impromptu game of charades in an effort to understand one another.

3. *Stress and Fatigue.* Science and common experience are on the same page when it comes to understanding the detrimental impact these factors have on the effectiveness of our communication. Both are insidious influences that can undermine our willingness and ability to engage with effectively with others.

4. *Inexperience.* We've all had the experience of being the "new kid," either at school or on the job. In such moments when we are sizing up a situation or the rules of the game in which we now find ourselves, we tend to be more reluctant to volunteer an opinion or objection than someone with more local knowledge and experience. Over the duration of your career as an aviator, you will have numerous opportunities to be the "new kid" and in each circumstance your perceived status as a rookie may make you less inclined to verbalize operational concerns. As the newbie you may be inclined to embrace a "seen but not heard" profile as you learn the ropes. This hesitancy can pollute the clarity necessary for a shared mental model when you are predisposed to withhold what you know or see.

This is only a partial list of the numerous factors that can pollute our communication and undermine its effectiveness. As you consider this list, I would encourage you to consider factors in your own life that can erode the quality of your communication with others.

The Biggest Pollutant

While each person's list of communication pollutants will vary, there is one that is common to us all, and that is the presence of bias. Bias sounds like a dirty word, and as much as we like to believe that its use applies only to those less enlightened than ourselves, the truth is that we all have one—or more—influences that hinder our ability to communicate effectively with others. Our personal values, experiences, and worldview can bias our willingness to engage with others in a manner that is meaningful and productive. There are those with whom we are less inclined to interact, and others with whom we are unwilling to engage altogether, and to the extent the strength of your personal views and opinions overpowers your ability to work alongside another person your ability to construct a shared mental model will be minimal at best.

Anyone who denies the fact that our biases flavor our interaction with others, both positively and negatively, is an idealist. The flight deck must be a sacred space in the sense that the ability to speak openly is not just an ideal, but an operational necessity, and the true demonstration of a professional is one who can resist the temptation to allow a personal bias to undermine the essential work necessary for mutual success. A professional can look beyond what makes us different in favor of focusing on what we need to do together in order to be successful.

The most dominant bias that influences our ability to communicate effectively with others is what I call *Transmit Bias*. The premise is simple and self-evident. Each of us wants to tell our own story more than we want to listen to someone else's. Each person's life is a story in which they are the central figure, and events are interpreted as a function of their impact on the main character. We are far more invested in the interests of the hero above those of other characters in the story and are far more inclined to view life and relationships through this prism.

Given that, ours is the narrative with which we are most familiar and about which we are most vocal. The evidence that supports this statement is both compelling and ever present. When you look at a group photo, whose image do you scan for first and foremost? Whose success story is the most important of all, and whose troubles are most deserving of a sympathetic ear?

In a general sense, have you ever noticed the amount of information people voluntarily share with total strangers? Bumper stickers and social media have become personal billboards on which we feel compelled to tell random strangers such things as:

- Where we go on vacation;
- Where we went to college and what we studied;
- Where our children go to school and their GPA;
- Our hobbies and interests;
- Our military affiliations—past and present;
- Who we voted for and what issues we support or oppose;
- How much blood we donated; and
- Where we shop.

Why the insistence on offering so much personal information about ourselves to people we don't even know? It's because of our desire for our story to be known, even if it hasn't been requested. This is the core essence of *Transmit Bias*.

Furthermore, social media has taught us to be exhibitionists of sorts in the sense that our lives can't be fully appreciated without the validation of others. The experience of being at the beach or enjoying a beautiful sunset is somehow brought to a new level of fulfillment by the knowledge that 2,500 people "liked" our pictures and descriptions of the moment.

A prime example of the influence of *Transmit Bias* can be found in the language we often use to initiate conversations. The use of phrases such as *"let's talk,"* or *"can we talk?"* emphasize the transmit side of the communication loop, and is motivated more by a desire to serve than to volley. These phrases suggest a desire for a monologue rather than a dialogue, and in these instances the invitation *"to talk"* is in reality an invitation to listen to what we have to say.

Another example of *Transmit Bias* is the satisfaction we derive from having the last word. We love it when ours are the words that leave others speechless and unable to return the volley. This "service ace" moment produces a sense of power that make it more likely that we will seek future opportunities for triumph. When a person is defined by such a quest their conversations can become hunting expeditions in search of trophies. To the extent you relish opportunities to silence others with the final word in a conversation your devotion to *Transmit Bias* will become stronger and your skill at conflict management will be nonexistent. The influence of our *Transmit Bias* is strong and often unyielding, and for that reason, we will go to great lengths to cast our hero in the best possible light as we communicate with others. The fish we caught gets bigger with every rendition of the story, and the difficulties associated with our particular struggles in life become more formidable over time.

Transmit Bias Makes Us Terrible Listeners

Listening is a critical component of effective communication, and to the extent your communication style is dominated by a strong *Transmit Bias*, your ability to relate to others in a meaningful and productive manner will be limited. While on a personal basis, the consequences of this lead to social isolation, on the flight deck it will become an operational impairment that can have disastrous consequences.

Listening requires a greater expenditure of cognitive energy on our part, and a conscious decision to shift the focus of the conversation from ourselves to someone else. For most, this is a challenge, and for some, it's impossible. Being an *engaged listener* requires that we allow our own story to be overshadowed by another, and this challenge is magnified in conversations for which our level of interest is minimal. A commitment to listening rather than speaking also involves an aspect of surrendering control in that we are no longer the one who chooses the topic of conversation. Not only do we not get to pick the story, but also we don't get to decide how it is told, and sometimes there is not even a cameo role for our favorite hero. Ouch. This arrangement is anathema to those whose desire to transmit exceeds their willingness to receive.

Hearing is omnidirectional in that we have the capacity to respond to audio stimuli from any direction or location within the range of our hearing. *Engaged listening*, on the other hand, is one-directional and requires that our focus be directed solely on the person who is talking—to the exclusion of any and all influences that would divert our attention. The fact that people typically speak at a rate of 140–180 words per minute and listen at 400 words per minute makes the temptation for our ears to stray off topic even stronger.

The process of engaging with others in a meaningful way can be further undermined by the fact that our listening skills are also biased. Here are three challenges to being an *engaged listener*.

1. People are biased in the direction of listening to that which we already believe to be true. This represents a significant barrier to effective communication in the sense that we are inclined to tune out when the conversation includes beliefs or opinions that challenge or differ from our own. *Cognitive dissonance* is the common term that defines this phenomenon. Communication becomes an exchange of words rather than ideas when either party refuses to listen. This type of bias can influence our decision-making when

we disregard operational information that undermines a course of action in which we are fully invested. This choice is the foundation of plan continuation errors that have contributed to decision-making errors associated with numerous CFIT/ALA mishaps.

2. We are also biased toward listening more intently to that which we can easily process and remember. Our brains crave order and simplicity, and this makes us more inclined to check out of conversations that are unnecessarily confusing or complex. (This is an important point to remember as you conduct a departure or approach briefing. The most effective briefings are thorough, clear, *and* concise.)

These are forms of communication *pollution* that often combine to make our listening selective at best. In the moments we find ourselves on the receiving end of a conversation about something with which we strongly disagree, find too complicated, or have no interest, the temptation to allow our attention to wander will be strongest. Here are some questions that will challenge you to consider the ease with which you can become a selective listener.

1. While others are saying something with which I disagree, am I giving consideration to the points they are making—or am I rehearsing a rebuttal that details all the reasons they are wrong? There is a distinct difference between actually listening to someone and simply waiting for your turn to talk. Allowing someone to share an opposing point of view does not equal agreement, but it does signal respect.

2. If the topic of conversation is more complicated than I deem necessary or tolerable, do I engage with the speaker in an effort to seek clarity, or do I pretend to listen while occupying my attention with other thoughts as I wait for them to finish?

3. If the topic of conversation is something for which I have little interest, do I listen politely and allow the other person their moment on center stage, or do I try to steer the conversation in a direction that is more suited to my own interests?

The remedy for this hindrance to effective communication is to master the discipline of becoming an *engaged listener*. What is meant by the term active listening, you ask? *Engaged listening* is the practice of making a conscious effort to listen carefully to the words being spoken but also focus with intent on the tone and body language that accompany their delivery.

Engaged listening is an important skill in life and the relationships that define it, but one that can be a life-and-death matter in a demanding and dynamic profession like aviation. In a general sense, how well we listen has a major impact on the quality of our personal relationships and ability to do our jobs effectively, and in the world of aviation, how well we listen can translate into our ability to operate the aircraft safely and effectively.

Given the strength of each person's transmit bias, *engaged listening* is an acquired skill whose development requires equal amounts of respect and self-discipline.

Here are the key elements of becoming an *engaged listener*:

1. Pay real attention. Not the pretend kind.

A. Look directly at the speaker. Focusing your attention on the person speaking to you creates a connection and demonstrates respect. Discipline yourself to not allow your eyes or your mind to wander. This includes the surreptitious glances at your phone that will not go unnoticed. When you divert your focus to another person or object, even for an instant, you are signaling a desire to search for a topic of greater interest.

> Selective listening means we tune in and out of a conversation as a function of how much it meets with our interest or approval. Selective listening is filtered listening. Flight safety demands *engaged listening.*

B. Put aside distracting thoughts. Remember, listeners have a higher word-count capacity than speakers, and for that reason, your brain is inclined to fill in the gaps with any and all manner of off-topic thoughts and distractions. Your mind will attempt to drive you in search for topics of greater interest, and when this happens the speaker's words become little more than background chatter. Recognize the moment when your mind starts to wander and redirect your attention to the ideas being expressed by the speaker.

C. Don't prepare your rebuttal while you are supposed to be listening. Of all the tell-tale signs of someone who is not fully invested in a conversation this is the most telling. Rehearsing all the reasons why the speaker is wrong is a clear indication of close-mindedness. Given that a closed mind has no interest in being open to learning something new, the result of this practice is the creation of a small world inhabited only by the very few whose opinions mirror your own. The practice of rehearsing your answer is the behavior of one who is hearing rather than listening.

D. Avoid external distractions. As mentioned earlier, the tendency is for your mind to wander during those moments when you are on the receiving end of conversations. *Engaged listening* is a multisensory discipline and requires mastery over your entire self. Boring conversations make our eyes look for other topics of interest, and our ears search the dial for more interesting stations. *Engaged listening* means full engagement. This is both a skill and a discipline that must be developed and reinforced with practice.

2. Show that you are tuned in.

A. Use your body language to signal interest in what the other person has to say. Nods, smiles, and a posture that is open and receptive signal interest and connection with the speaker. An occasional and appropriate verbal acknowledgment also goes a long way toward conveying a genuine level of respect for what the other person has to say.

3. Actively participate with the speaker.

A. Your primary role as an *engaged listener* is to accurately decipher what you are being told. A lack of interest or personal bias may attempt to flavor your interpretation of the messages you receive, and for this reason, it is often helpful to engage the speaker with questions in an effort to be fully committed to the conversation. Here are some examples:

"Are you saying ___?"
- *"I think you're telling me____. Am I understanding correctly?"*

B. Statements and questions that demonstrate empathy with the speaker are also useful tools for developing the skill of active listening.

For example:
"What was that like?"
- *"That must have been incredibly difficult."*

4. Wait your turn to talk.

A. Interrupting someone in order to counter their arguments

or steer the conversation in a direction more to your liking is the behavior of one who lacks self-discipline. Interruptions are rude displays of social dominance that hijack the communication loop by attempting to silence one of its participants. Interrupting a speaker is a form of verbal arm wrestling that signals a need to control the conversation. If you are predisposed to interrupt or butt in, it's clear you aren't fully devoted to the discipline of listening..

5. Don't disrespect the speaker.

A. There is an inner cynic who resides in us all. This little troll longs for the opportunity to put others in their place, especially when you are in the presence of an audience whose approval you desire. One of the goals of *engaged listening* is to gain insight into the thoughts and perspectives of another. As such, you must quell your inner cynic's desire to take the verbal cheap shot in response to their opinion, and whatever points you may score with your sarcasm will be overshadowed by how small such behavior makes you look. If you have a different opinion, be mature and respectful enough to verbalize it in a thoughtful manner at an appropriate time. You never look bigger in the process of trying to make someone else look smaller.

> Trying to make someone else look small doesn't make you look bigger.

Flight safety requires effective communication with those strapped in next to you on the flight deck and with those with whom you share a radio frequency. Effective communication requires an equal commitment to speaking *and* listening, and self-discipline is essential for both.

> Effective communication is a two-way street and it works best when both lanes are open.

COMMUNICATION

Chapter 9

Be Precise

Know How to Speak the Language of Safety

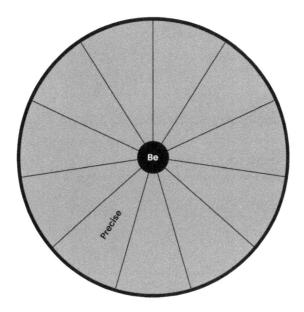

The influence of the three elements used by your encryption and decryption software—words, tone, and body language—is altered significantly in your exchanges with ATC. It is in these instances when you are communicating with a nameless and faceless human at the other end of an assigned frequency that the influence of the most critical component of your decryption software is removed from the equation, and you are forced to rely on spoken words and tone as the sole metrics for interpretation.

Speaking the language of safety involves a commitment to choosing your words and tone with care and precision in situations in which your most important interpretative tool is unavailable.

Words ☑
Tone ☑
Body Language ☑

Words ☑
Tone ☑
Body Language ✕

These images underscore this point and are intended to emphasize the critical importance of precision with regard to our exchanges with those we cannot see. When the most dominant and insightful aspect of your communication software is unavailable, flight safety demands that you exercise discipline with regard to your choice of words and the manner with which they are delivered.

The truth of this statement was demonstrated in the findings of a paper published by the Flight Safety Foundation[2] that identified the factors that most often contribute to the types of communication errors that result in accidents and violations.

Let's take a look at these common errors and discuss some strategies to prevent their use on your frequencies"

1. Ambiguous communication
2. Nonstandard phraseology
3. Regional differences
4. Call sign confusion
5. Readback-hearback
6. English language proficiency
7. Code switching

---

[2] Wilson, Dale. "Failure to Communicate, Hearing—and Understanding—the Spoken Word Is Crucial to Safe Flight." Flight Safety Foundation Aero Safety World, October 2016.

1. Ambiguous communication. This refers to situations in which the words or phrases we use can have more than one possible meaning. Numbers are particularly problematic in the creation of ambiguity, especially when homophones are used. Homophones are two words that sound the same but have different meanings. In aviation, use of the words *two/to and four/for* are especially troublesome, and extra care should be given to transmissions in which these common words are used.

An accident in which the use of homophones resulted in ambiguous communication between a flight crew and ATC and was a causal factor in a preventable tragedy occurred during an exchange between a Flying Tiger B747 (Flight 66) and Approach Control at Kuala Lumpur in February 1989. The B-747 impacted a hill near the airport after misinterpreting a descent clearance. Here is the critical part of the conversation that created the fatal ambiguity:

ATC: *"Tiger 66, descend two four zero zero, cleared for NDB approach Runway 33."*

Tiger 66: *"Okay, cleared four zero zero."*

The controller transmitted a clearance for the aircraft to descend to an altitude of 2,400 FT to commence the approach, but the crew interpreted this as a clearance to descend **to** 400 FT above sea level, a clearance that was actually 2000 feet too low! This was an experienced crew who was very familiar with operations into this airport, and to this day questions remain as to why they interpreted and accepted the controller's instructions as a clearance to descend to such a low altitude. Equally curious is the fact that this confusion was not addressed or clarified by ATC.

In an effort to eliminate confusion or ambiguity in you communication with ATC, adopt a practice of attaching appropriate words to the numbers used in your transmission. For example, rather than saying, *"turn left to 230, maintain 180,"* say *"turn left to **heading** 230, maintain 180 **knots**."*

Given the fact that virtually every exchange with ATC includes the use of both words and numbers, it is imperative the instructions you receive or the intentions you express are clearly understood by both parties. Whenever you have doubts about either you must proactively reconcile any doubts. Whenever there is unresolved doubt, there is the potential for danger. In situations in which there is confusion regarding the specifics of clearance, there is always the option to spell out words using the phonetic alphabet. For example, a clearance to *"proceed direct to FURBO intersection"* could be clarified by responding, *"Understand we are cleared direct to Foxtrot Uniform Romeo Bravo Oscar."*

With regard to your understanding of your communication with ATC, clarity is essential.
Transmit with purpose. Listen with intent.
Doubt = Danger.

Furthermore, an awareness of your operating environment is imperative as a means of verifying and cross-checking the context and proper application of instructions from ATC. Know your surroundings and be able to discern when a clearance makes sense given your location or altitude. Such clarity is especially critical when operating at low altitudes in terminal areas in which high terrain may be a factor.

2. Nonstandard phraseology. The intentional use of terminology that is nonstandard and whose meaning can be lost on others on the frequency is a very common communication error that invites confusion. Slang is a good example of this type of nonstandard phraseology and its use on an operational frequency is both counterproductive and unprofessional. Be ever mindful of the fact that your transmissions are heard not only by the controller but also everyone else on the frequency, and for this reason the opportunity for confusion can become magnified with the use of phraseology that is not commonly understood.

I recall an instance when we shared a frequency with a Pan Am B 747 as we were both being sequenced for arrival into Buenos Aires. The weather was at minimums, and the approach control radar was out of service. Given the fact that neither aircraft had eyes on the other and ATC couldn't see either of us, I recall the care and precision with which each crew read back clearance instructions but also updated their position as we both maneuvered in the blind toward the same piece of concrete. The clarity provided by our position reports enabled the creation of a shared mental model of our positions relative to one another and the Initial Approach Fix (IAF) and reinforced the importance of standard phraseology.

As with any profession, aviation has its own vocabulary and among pilots there is often a cultural variance that exists between military and civilian organizations with regard to their individual and unique forms of verbal SOP. Because of this, confusion can easily arise when terms that are unique to one culture are used in the company of another. For example, if a clearance from an approach controller at a civilian airport to *"Descend to 6,000 FT"* is issued to a military pilot who then reads it back as *"Roger, descend to Angels 6,"* there is the possibility that the controller, as well as other crews on the frequency, will be left to wonder regarding this pilot's intention. While the use of such casual language may be automatic on the part of the military crew and acceptable in the context of operation at their home base, its use in another arena invites doubt and is therefore a potential threat to safety.

NOTE: The "coolness factor" often associated with military aviation jargon loses its charm in the civilian environment—quickly. An array of not-so-flattering adjectives will be assigned to those who insist on inserting military "coolspeak" into their exchanges with civilian controllers. English words, the clear and precise kind we were taught in school, are the universal language of aviation and each crew must pursue linguistic purity in every transmission. The use of slang certainly has its place in the culture of aviation and while its use can certainly be appropriate in interpersonal conversations within your organization, remember that when you key the mic to go public its use has the potential to undermine safety. Be proactive and disciplined with regard to your commitment to using standard aviation phraseology in every transmission on every frequency.

> The use of nonstandard phraseology such as slang in your exchanges with ATC can fill the frequency with confusion. Verbal SOP is the language of safety.

3. Regional differences. In different parts of the world, or within distinct areas of the same country, it is often the case that a variety of words can be used to convey the same idea. This phenomenon is different from the use of slang in that in these cases, the variations of words and phrases are codified in the official regulatory language of that particular country or region. While English is the standard language of aviation worldwide, there still exists some variation in different parts of the world with regard to the words and phrases used to convey a similar message. In these instances, it can be said that we are using the same vocabulary but with a different dictionary. For example, a decision to discontinue an approach will be called a *go-around* in most parts of the world, while in some locations, the word *overshoot* will be used to communicate the same intention. Different terms, same meaning.

> There may be times when you understand the words being spoken to you but not the meaning they convey. Be proactive in your quest for clarity when the message is unclear.
> Doubt = Danger.

Such variations also exist among different branches of the US military. For example, when I was in the navy, our standard entry procedure into the airport traffic pattern on a VFR day was known as *entering the break*. This was SOP at navy bases and involved flying over the field at 1,200 FT and making a sharp bank to the left to enter the traffic pattern. On my first flight to an air force base, after a hand-off from approach control, I checked in with the tower and reported the field in sight, at which time I was *"cleared for a left pitchout."* I had not heard this phrase before, and though I had a general idea of what I had been cleared to do, my brain did a momentary search of its communication files in order to clarify my doubts. As it turned out, the guy in my back seat was a grizzled veteran who spoke fluent air force, and he confirmed my hunch before I could key the mic to query the tower controller for a navy translation of my clearance.

While local knowledge and experience will greatly enhance your ability to decipher the meanings associated with regional differences in phraseology, in those moments when you have doubts about what you've been instructed or cleared to do, it is *always* a good idea to ask for clarification. *Always.*

4. Call-sign confusion. Think of your call sign as your operational name, as this is how you will be identified and addressed in every exchange on every frequency. Just as with your personal identification, your call sign has both a first and last name, for example, *"FedEx 1224"* or *"United 2332"*. The need to pay close attention to the use of your operational name on every frequency is critical, and inattention creates unnecessary confusion and delays in subsequent transmissions with other aircraft on your frequency. In a high-density airport, not responding when your name is called takes the controller's time and attention away from the task of managing other aircraft and detracts from both the safety and efficiency of the system.

When operating on a designated company frequency, it is customary for everyone involved in the operation to have the same first name, and in the interest of efficiency it is appropriate to communicate on a last-name basis. Because everyone else on the frequency has the same first name, using only the last name *"1224"* is efficient and unlikely to cause confusion.

While this practice may be useful in operations around home base, uncertainty can enter the picture when it is employed on frequencies shared by multiple aircraft from different carriers. Unnecessary confusion is introduced into the mix when *"FedEx 1224"* and *"United 1224"* are on the same frequency and choose to identify themselves only by their last names as they respond to transmissions from ATC. While controllers should advise both aircraft when another aircraft with a similar call sign is on the frequency, this reminder can be overlooked during periods of high-density or high-tempo operations, and it is incumbent for each crew to exercise discipline on the frequency by using both their first and last operational names in their transmissions on common frequencies.

> Safety demands the use of your first and last names in every transmission on common frequencies. Reserve your use of verbal shorthand for designated company frequencies.

5. Readback/Hearback. Accuracy is a critical component of the communication between the flight deck and ATC and must be pursued with regard to the details of what you heard *and* what you read back. This accuracy requires the discipline to listen with intent to the details and specifics of what you are being told and to confirm the message with equal attention. Think of a verbal clearance from ATC as a story about where you will go and what you will do. Endeavor to tell the story exactly as you heard it.

Readback and hearback errors refer to those occasions when the crew or the controller repeats a clearance incorrectly (readback), and the error is not caught by the controller (hearback). This type of error was a contributing factor in the confusion that resulted from the exchange between the crew of Tiger 66, and the ensuing disaster might have been prevented if either the crew or ATC had proactively addressed the uncertainty that was introduced during their fatal exchange.

A variety of factors can contribute to this type of communication breakdown. Confusion can be caused by the presence of more than one aircraft on the frequency with similar call signs, the use of verbal shorthand and nonstandard phraseology, and in some cases, the error may be the result of a simple slip of the tongue that is not caught by either party.

It is also noteworthy that with experience can come the development of a bias toward what we expect to hear as opposed to what is actually being said. Crews who fly the same route or operate from the same airports on a regular basis become accustomed to hearing the same instructions at specific points and can develop a tendency to hear what they expect rather than what is actually being said. In these instances, SA can become compromised, as a crew's shared mental model is based on an over-reliance on past experience to the exclusion of an accurate assessment of what is actually happening or being said. A shared mental model that allows an over-reliance on experience and expectations to be the primary tools for its construction is seriously flawed. This over-reliance is a type of *Groundhog Day Syndrome* in reference to the movie in which Bill Murray's character relived the same day over and over to the point of knowing the details of conversations and events before they happened. His experience had taught him exactly what to expect, and while it was humorous to watch as this level of SA enabled him to predict future events and work to orchestrate different outcomes, there is a lesson to be learned that has an application to flight safety and *Proactive Flying*.

Groundhog Day Syndrome is an insidious condition that develops when we allow our experience to be seen as the sole predictive template for future events. In these instances vigilance gives way to complacency and readback/hearback errors between ATC and a crew are warning signs of its influence over the operational mindset that characterizes your flight deck. *Groundhog Day Syndrome* erodes the practice of *Proactive Flying* through its false assurance that things to come will transpire as they always have.

Experience is a wonderful teacher whose steady hand of assurance and predictability can certainly build our confidence, but there is a dark side that can develop when we allow our operational memory bank and its operational predictions to eclipse our ability to discern even the most subtle deviations from what we have come to expect. Once this level of acceptance has become the basis for our shared mental model, there is an inability to hear instructions that are at odds with those we have received with great regularity in past situations, and we are more inclined to hear and act on the basis of what our experience has taught us to expect. Such is are the habits of the *dangerously good*. When we allow this to happen we become selectively blind and deaf to that which we don't expect and our ability to make sound decisions is compromised.

> Experience is a wonderful tutor, but don't allow it to be the sole influence that defines your expectations. This can skew the accuracy of your shared mental model.

As an example of this, I am reminded of an event in which a readback/hearback error was a causal factor that enticed an experienced crew to land on the wrong runway. This particular crew had flown together on the same route for an entire month, and in fifteen previous instances, their routine had been exactly the same. After a handoff from approach control to the tower, they would report the airport in sight, at which time they would be told that they were *"cleared for a visual approach to RWY **36L**."* The same clearance for a visual approach to the same runway had been issued by the same controller on fifteen previous trips. On day sixteen, however, things developed according to a different plan.

Everything about this trip was a *Groundhog Day* experience up to the moment approach control handed them off to the tower. After checking in with the tower and reporting that they had the airport in sight, the crew was *"cleared for a visual approach to RWY **36R**."* They acknowledged the clearance by saying, *"Roger, cleared for the visual to RWY **36L**,"* the very same approach they had come to expect as a result of their recent pattern of experience. The controller failed to catch the error in their readback and didn't realize that they were lined up for the wrong runway until the aircraft was on short final. The tone of the tower controller's command to *"go around"* introduced a degree of urgency that caught the crew off guard, and they were shocked to realize that they had almost landed on the wrong runway. Fortunately, there was no immediate conflict with other aircraft on the ground or in the pattern, and safety was not jeopardized. There were, however, lots of red faces and unnecessary paperwork for everybody. Filling out safety reports and receiving invitations meetings you would rather not attend have a way of drawing the kind of attention that should be avoided at all costs.

Listen to every clearance as though you were hearing it for the very first time, and endeavor to read it back exactly as it was received. A simple *"roger"* is never a satisfactory response for a clearance readback, as this type of verbal shorthand affords no assurance that what was said and what was heard are the same.

6. English language proficiency. Anyone who has traveled abroad can attest to the difficulties that can arise when speaking to people whose proficiency in your own language is lacking. Add a strong dose of accent, and a simple exchange can revert to a lot of talking and repeating yourself with a louder tone, as if that will provide additional clarity. Given the absence of your ability to point to pictures or invite the aid of an interpreter when talking to controllers whose proficiency in English may be lacking, you are forced to rely only on your ability to interpret the spoken words. There are instances in which this process of interpretation will include requests to *"say again,"* followed by a conference between the members of the crew as they attempt to decode what is being said. These are certainly occasions when experience is your friend, and an advanced level of knowledge and familiarity with the environment in which you are operating is a helpful tool in attempting to achieve a high level of accuracy and understanding.

As a general rule, when talking to controllers whose native tongue is not English, it is important to speak slowly and enunciate clearly. The practice of speed talking that may serve you well in your exchanges with New York Center or O'Hare ground controllers won't be the least bit helpful in your interaction with Buenos Aires approach control.

In *no case* is it a good idea to use slang when speaking to controllers whose native tongue is not English. Many of these individuals have been trained to achieve a level of English proficiency that is based on the use of the specific words and phrases of the aviation system. In other words, they have been trained to converse in the language of the verbal SOP that is set forth in the regulatory guidelines of the governing bodies of aviation. The degree of confusion referenced earlier with regard to the use of slang is magnified exponentially when such verbal shortcuts are employed during an exchange with a controller for whom English is a second language.

> Slang and speed talking never advance the interests of clarity or safety when communicating with a controller whose native tongue is not English.

7. Code switching. This phenomenon is a common occurrence with people who are multilingual. When the pressures of stress or fatigue are present there is a natural tendency for such people to revert to basic learned behaviors in terms of their speech patterns. Code switching occurs when the stress of the moment prompts our brain to seek order and simplicity with the use of the familiar speech and linguistic patterns of our native tongue. When this occurs, grammar and syntax can be rearranged in such a way as to add confusion to what is being said through the introduction of expressions that have double meanings. Unilingual individuals (that would include most Americans) can also revert to code switching during times of stress. Such occurrences typically involve the unconscious practice of inserting colloquialisms of everyday language or rearranging our syntax in professional conversations. It is in these moments when stress squeezes our brains that we are apt to invent new words of our own to describe something or mix words of familiarity with those of formality as we attempt to make sense of a situation.

Code switching was almost certainly a factor in the Tenerife accident. The KLM FO's final words, "We are now at takeoff," were spoken during a highly stressful situation in which his uncertainty regarding their takeoff clearance was exacerbated by the reality that the captain was advancing the throttles. In that moment, the FO switched his Dutch and English grammar in such a way that the meaning of his message was unclear to the Spanish controllers in the tower who understood him to mean that he was in a position to take off, and not that the aircraft was actually commencing its roll down the runway. Investigators replayed these words of the KLM FO countless times during the months that followed the accident, and there was great debate as to the true meaning and intent of this message. Low visibility at the airport made it impossible for the controllers to have an accurate picture of what was happening on the runway, and they were left with their assumptions regarding the KLM crew's intentions.

Speak the Language of Safety

Proactive Flying requires an awareness of the common errors in communication between flight crews and ATC, and a commitment to comply with the verbal SOP of the industry in every exchange. The absence of the nonverbal messages that exercise great influence over the quality of our communication makes it absolutely essential that we choose our words and tone with precision. Furthermore, to the extent that we allow our verbal or listening skills to be employed in a manner that prioritizes expediency over accuracy, we are eroding the foundation of our shared mental model in a manner that undermines flight safety.

Here are some guidelines for your communication with those who are strapped in next to you on the flight deck and those at the other end of the mic. I call them the "4 Bes of Effective Communication," and to the extent they become part of your own verbal SOP, your ability to reap the safety benefits of an accurate shared mental model will be enhanced.

1. **Be precise.**
2. **Be succinct.**
3. **Be timely.**
4. **Be acknowledged**.

1. Be precise. Choosing your words with care and precision is a strong antidote for ambiguity. Precision in your communication requires the self-discipline to adhere to the standard phraseology of the industry and identify yourself with both your first and last operational names. Furthermore, as stated earlier, when your transmission includes both words and numbers, ensure that they are joined together in a manner that offers clarity regarding your position and your intentions. Precision requires that you say exactly what is necessary to convey an accurate and complete message. Avoid verbal shorthand such as slang and incomplete call signs, and be mindful of the fact that whenever you transmit a message to ATC, you are also speaking to every other aircraft on the frequency. To the extent your transmission lacks compliance with the standards of the industry, or is incomplete, you will likely undermine the SA of other crews on your frequency.

Precision is also required at the listening end of these conversations, and it is a good idea for you to pay close attention to the exchanges between the controller and other aircraft on your frequency. This affords you the opportunity to gather useful information about their position relative to yours and such things as ride reports along your route of flight, or the winds at a different altitude. This type of eavesdropping is especially important during operations in the terminal area and will help you develop and maintain a dynamic mental picture of the location and direction of movement of other aircraft relative to your position. This practice greatly enhances your SA as you develop a comprehension of who is where on and around the airport.

> The use of verbal shorthand such as slang and incomplete call signs on common frequencies undermines flight safety.

With regard to the verbal exchanges on the flight deck, checklist discipline and standard callouts are examples that illustrate the importance of precision. There are words and phrases that we expect to say and hear during the evolution of the flight, and deviations from those expectations introduce ambiguity and confusion. During a demanding phase of flight such as the takeoff roll and initial climb out, each member of the crew has the expectation of hearing specific callouts at predetermined points, and safety will be compromised at the worst possible moment if one of them chooses to deviate from the standard script. Safety demands adherence to the verbal SOP of checklists and standard callouts, and even the smallest deviation invites confusion. This kind of behavior demonstrates poor judgment and a lack of discipline, and choosing to add your own "personal touch" to these critical exchanges replaces the precision and certainty necessary for flight safety with ambiguity and confusion that will undermine it.

2. Be succinct. In aviation, there is a learning curve that every student pilot must navigate when it comes to the process of talking on the radio. Though the act of encoding and expressing your words is one that you have developed and practiced since you were very young, there is something about knowing how to to engage in a verbal exchange with a nameless and faceless voice at the other end of the line. Add the expectation to use technical and operational terms with which you may not yet be completely familiar, and the whole process can be intimidating. I remember my early flights as a student pilot and the confusion that would scramble my brain's ability to speak in complete and coherent sentences when keying the microphone to transmit a message. It's funny now to look back on these moments, and I can promise that you will have similar experiences. It's part of the learning curve, and rest assured it gets easier as your logbook expands.

An important step in overcoming this stage fright was to develop the practice of taking a moment to mentally rehearse exactly what I wanted to say before keying the mic. A key part of this process involved figuring out the words that would offer clarity and precision to my message and learning how to use as few of them as necessary. This is one area in which confidence grew as a result of experience and more than a few embarrassing moments when I got tongue-tied or offered a rambling paragraph when a short statement would do just fine. I had a crusty old instructor in the navy who once told me, *"Son, you don't get extra points for the number of words you use."*

Remember, there are usually multiple aircraft on the same frequency, and only one person can speak at a time. These important transmissions are for the purpose of informing others of your position and intentions and not offering them an explanation about things they don't need to know. With regard to your transmissions with ATC and other aircraft, make it your goal to inform more and explain less.

Be mindful that every moment your mic is keyed is a moment that controllers and other crews on the same frequency are forced to wait their turn to speak. What they have to say is equally important, so it is both considerate and operationally imperative that you learn to economize your words. Don't be a frequency hog.

Being succinct means that you say what is necessary to convey your message with accuracy and precision while using the fewest number of words possible. In this arena, brevity is your friend. Develop the practice of focusing on exactly what you want to say and how you want to say it before keying the mic. It gets easier with time and practice.

> Being succinct means that you say what is necessary to convey your message with accuracy and precision while using the fewest number of words. Brevity is your friend.

3. Be timely. Aviation is both complex and dynamic, and there are many times when you don't have the luxury of taking a wait-and-see approach to verbalizing your concerns. Being timely means saying what *needs* to be said *when* it needs to be heard by others. The best time to verbalize a concern about the presence of a threat to safety is the moment it comes to your attention. Say it *when* you see it, not later, and not maybe.

This hesitation to verbalize operational doubts in favor of simply watching and hoping it all works out is often rooted in a lack of self-confidence and a fear of looking foolish if your concerns turn out to be much ado about nothing. Let me say that while I have memories of the times I regretted not speaking up, I have no such misgivings about the times I did—even when it turned out that my concerns were unfounded. A little embarrassment is an acceptable price to pay in the pursuit of safety, and to my knowledge embarrassment has never been cited as a causal factor in an accident. As stated earlier, in those instances when you are wrestling with the choice between speaking up and holding your tongue, the fact that you are even having this conversation with yourself is usually a pretty reliable indicator that you need to weigh in sooner than later.

> Being timely means saying *what* needs to be said *when* safety needs to hear it.

4. Be acknowledged. Communication works best when it is bidirectional and complete. This means that your encryption and decryption software has done its best to ensure that both parties have a mutual understanding of the messages being shared between them. Not responding in a timely manner to what you are being told, or offering one-word responses in situations in which clarity demands a more detailed confirmation create circumstances that invite ambiguity and confusion. Every operational statement demands a timely and appropriate response. The failure to meet this requirement represents unfinished business and is an invitation for doubt to take a seat on the flight deck.

Being acknowledged involves a commitment to ensuring closure to each exchange and recognizing that failing to do so invites doubt. Be certain that you have been heard and properly understood. Every interactive exchange both on the flight deck and with those on the other end of a selected frequency must be acknowledged in a timely and effective manner that ensures mutual understanding regarding the accuracy of the message and the intentions of all involved.

> Be certain that you have been heard and understood. Communication is most effective when it is bidirectional and acknowledged.

As stated earlier, in these early and developmental days of your aviation career, the amount of concentration and mental investment required to engage with ATC is such that there are times we will be tempted to allow it to take priority over other considerations, and there will be times when talking on the radio will seem like the most critical matter at hand. It is not.

Dealing with an inflight systems anomaly or an amendment to your flight plan will often prompt a desire to elevate the need for a conversation about the situation to the top of your list of important steps. On these occasions you must resist this temptation and remember that flying the airplane takes priority over a conversation. Always.

While effective communication is critical to flight safety, nothing takes priority over flying the airplane. If you remember only one thing from this book, make it this: There is an operational hierarchy in aviation that must be followed any and every time you are strapped in and the engines are running. Here are your priorities when a change of plans or circumstances introduces an element of operational jazz. These priorities, *Aviate*, *Navigate*, and *Communicate*, are the closest thing to operational commandments that I can offer and should always be applied in the order in which they appear. Always.

1. Aviate. *Fly the airplane.* Make sure the aircraft's speed, altitude, and configuration are appropriate for your situation. If you are flying as part of a crew, have a brief conversation that clearly establishes individual roles and responsibilities. The first priority for this exchange is to determine who is flying the aircraft. *"You have the airplane." "Roger, I have the airplane,"* is a good place to start. It's just that simple, and it's also just that important.

2. Navigate. *Know where you are and where you are going.* The value of ensuring aircraft control can seem incidental if you lose confidence in your awareness of where you are and where you are going. Make sure that both members of the crew have a shared mental model of your present position, direction, and engagement of the appropriate navigation mode for the situation.

3. Communicate. *Key the mic only after steps 1 and 2 are completed.* Only after the requirements to aviate and navigate are satisfied can you talk to someone about what is happening. If you are being pressured for a response prior to the completion of the first two steps, a request for the controller to *"stand by"* is both appropriate and advisable. While communication with outside agencies is necessary and important, it must wait for its turn in line.

In aviation, there is an operational hierarchy that must be observed in every situation:
1. Aviate 2. Navigate 3. Communicate.
In that order. Always.

Chapter 10

Be a Mediator

Know How to Manage Conflict

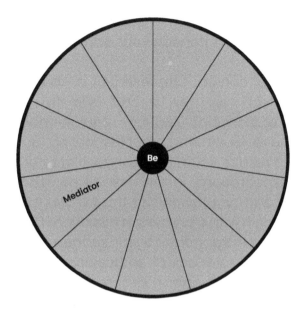

The mention of conflict management in the context of a discussion of the skills that enhance crew effectiveness and flight safety may strike some as evidence of the "touchy-feely" nature of CRM and as confirmation of the mistaken belief that the primary objective of CRM is to encourage everyone to "be nice and get along." Over the course of the years that I conducted CRM training at my airline, I came to understand that this was a common and enduring belief among many of our seasoned pilots, and conversations with my CRM counterparts at other airlines confirmed my suspicion that this opinion was shared by many in the industry.

Let me counter this common belief by stating a simple fact that will serve as the guiding principle of this chapter: The presence of interpersonal conflict on the flight deck is one of the strongest and most corrosive hindrances to effective communication, and a failure to manage it in a timely manner represents a threat to safety. Managing conflict refers to a process that requires a willingness to acknowledge its presence in your midst and a proactive engagement with the other party to ensure that it doesn't impede your ability to work together.

Interpersonal conflict represents a breakdown in a relationship. Much like the aircraft we fly, personal and professional relationships require regular maintenance. As such, they require monitoring, troubleshooting, and sometimes, repair. Conflict results when someone violates our personal or professional expectations. In the case of personal conflict, the transgressions can be unknown to the violator and in this case resolution will begin with a process of discovery. Discernible shifts in the relationship characterized by the sudden onset of the "silent treatment" or a notable lack of enthusiasm on the part of the other person are reliable signs that something is amiss between you. In these instances it often becomes the responsibility of the offending party to assume the role of detective as they set about gathering the evidence that identifies the root of the problem. All you may know is that the other person has gone dark and their unwillingness to provide specifics about the offense that prompted their retreat means that you must take the initiative to repair what has been broken.

A good first step in this process of discovery is to ask a simple question such as, *"Have I done something to offend you?"* Such an inquiry must be offered with humility and sincerity and can not include elements of tone or body language that suggest a sense of duty or compulsion. A tone suggesting sarcasm or non-verbal cues that convey exasperation will be counterproductive. The process of reconciliation is greatly enhanced when the offended party responds to this overture by recounting the offense in a mature and straightforward manner. Such a response puts the ball of reconciliation in play and provides an opportunity to repair the breach in the relationship. The way a person responds to an honest and open inquiry about the nature of the offense is telling and provides key insight regarding their desire for reconciliation.

An emotional barrage of accusations or a coy challenge to dig deeper for clues are signals that they want to make the offending party pay for their mistakes and a suitable price has yet to be established. In this instance conflict management can become a transactional arrangement in which the currency is pain and the offended party demands the right to determine when sufficient payment has been made.

There is a sense in which people regard relationships as transactional in nature and there is an economy of giving and getting that often defines how people interact with one another. Maintaining accounts of who is giving and who is getting, who is owed payment, and who has acquired more or less than the other feeds the corrosive practice of comparison that turns us into scorekeepers who are forever committed to knowing who is winning or losing.

Our language is flavored with verbiage that illustrates the degree to which we view our relationships with others as accounts to be managed. Here are some examples of everyday phrases that underscore this point:

"You owe me/I owe you"
"After all I've done for you this is how you repay me?"
"I expected more from you."
And of course we all know about the promise of *"payback."*

Given this common practice a critical component of conflict management is the ability to emphasize *what* is right rather than *who* is right. To the extent we are committed to balancing the debits and credits of interpersonal accounts our chance for a satisfactory resolution to the impasse will be nonexistent.

The goal of conflict management on the flight deck is not the cultivation of friendships or the creation of an environment in which all parties see the world exactly the same way. Instead, its purpose is to ensure that interpersonal differences are not permitted to impede a crew's commitment to the objectives of safety, legality, and reliability. You need not be friends in order to be an effective crew, but you must be able to rise above the differences that have the potential to hinder your ability to work together as a team. The ability to do so is a characteristic of a professional.

At a basic human level, unresolved conflict erodes and eventually eliminates altogether our desire to interact with those individuals we perceive to be standing in the opposite corner of the ring. While on a personal level this has the potential to damage relationships, its presence in the professional arena threatens the safety of the operation.

Unresolved conflict is an operational cancer whose treatment cannot be administered with a passive hope that it will simply go away on its own with the passage of time. Such a hope is not grounded in reality, but more given to a type of fantasy that wishes that aggressive cancers can be treated effectively with the use of passive remedies. Time and inattention are ineffective treatments for this extreme form of communication *pollution* and to the extent there is unresolved conflict with the person strapped in beside you at the conclusion of a flight, it will define the operational tone of subsequent flights together. This is true whether your next flight occurs one week or one year from now, and in these instances unfinished business from previous experiences with the other person will adversely influence the quality of your communication. Your conversations will tend to be perfunctory and obligatory and conducted with the minimum effort necessary for the completion of required tasks. The operational enthusiasm that typically prompts a desire to look out for the interests and welfare of all will give way to a glum determination to simply hunker down and gut it out with the minimum amount of interaction. The long-term effects of the unfinished business of unresolved conflict can pay adverse dividends for an extended period of time, and there is no expiration date on its ability to undermine a crew's ability to manage threats to safety. Grudges have a long memory that grants quick and easy access to the hard feelings that have been nursed and indulged over time, and the longer we place our hope in the passive remedies of hope and time the stronger and more destructive this operational cancer can become.

Know the Two Types of Conflict

Whenever we hear the word *conflict* there is a common tendency to invoke images of angry encounters, but at a basic level conflict begins quietly in the disappointment of unmet interpersonal expectations. While such differences can certainly escalate to flared nostrils and clenched fists, their inception begins in our hearts and minds. The seeds of interpersonal conflict are sewn in the failure of others behave or perform according to our personal or professional expectations, and take root when their actions repress our desire to communicate with that person. The presence of conflict can often be insidious and its corrosive influence over our ability to work together is both gradual and progressive. It is often the case that its presence is first recognized by a noticeable shift in the tone, frequency, or nature of your conversations, and in some cases, the interaction between you and the other person ceases altogether. Picking up on these cues is an important aspect of the interpersonal skill required to understand how to begin the process of resolution, and while some are more adept at others in this regard, even the most socially obtuse can usually recognize the deafening sound of the silent treatment.

The types of conflict you will encounter in aviation fall into two categories—*personal* and professional. Generally speaking, *personal* expectations have to do with the individual standards you expect of another and can include such things as their appearance, conduct, and demeanor. The *professional* expectations we have of others apply to the performance of their duties and include such things as knowledge, proficiency, and SOP compliance. Oftentimes the distinction between these two types of conflict can become blurred and there can be an overlap between the two. For example, poor grooming habits or a sloppy uniform are contrary to both our *personal* and *professional* expectations.

Both types of conflict are equally grounded in an unsatisfactory comparison between what we expect of the other person and what we observe and experience, and it is important to note that left unresolved, either type of conflict will likely become the other. Personal friction will impair your ability to work with the other person on a professional basis, and professional discord that results from how the other person operates will foster feelings of personal resentment or disrespect.

The good news is that regardless of the type of conflict you experience, the prescription for managing it is the same for each. Before we examine the specific steps for managing conflict, let's take a brief quiz that may offer some personal insights regarding your experience and understanding of the complex and often subtle nature of interpersonal conflict.

1. Conflict is always the other person's fault.
   True or False?

2. I can avoid conflict altogether if I am nice to everybody.
   True or False?

3. The best way to deal with conflict is:
   A. Say nothing and avoid the other person as much as possible.
   B. Pretend it isn't an issue and let someone else handle it.

C. Say something, but carefully and indirectly so as not to make things worse.
D. Figure out who is on your side before doing anything.
E. Talk directly to the person with whom you have the conflict.

4. When attempting to resolve a conflict with someone, it is important to:
A. Hash things out in public so there will be witnesses.
B. Get as many people on your side as possible.
C. Find an appropriate time and location to talk.
D. Interact via text or social media rather than face-to-face.
E. Make sure you are emotionally charged in order to gain the advantage.

Let's grade the quiz.

1. Conflict is always the other person's fault.
False

Life is like a dance, and while the steps that define it must be performed in an ordered fashion and in conjunction with another person, there is often great latitude among individuals about its execution. Our preferences with regard to the amount of flair or technique that should be applied to a particular movement can become sources of conflict when they become the standard we expect of others. Elevating our personal methods to the level of SOP for all is both selfish and unrealistic. Recalling the influence of *Transmit Bias* it is clear that we like having things done our way and are given to pointing the fingers of blame for the presence of conflict at those who can't or won't comply with our wishes.

In these instances, the notion of who should bear the blame for a dispute is frequently based on a need to distance oneself from accountability. The practice of placing blame in the context of managing conflict will quickly shift attention away from *what* is right or mutually agreeable to *who* is right (or wrong) and whose preferences will carry the day.

Conflict management is not about winning or being right, but is focused on finding the common ground that will enable you to work together to achieve a common objective. To the extent you have an overdeveloped need to be right or to win, it is likely that your ability to accept your expectations as contributing factors to the presence of the conflict will be nonexistent. The need to win can become almost pathological, and for some, there will come a point in the exchange where they will dig in their heels to defend a position that is illogical or not based on fact rather than admitting an error. Continued engagement with those who elevate their own opinions to the level of fact or science and are unwilling to concede or accept errors in their understanding of the facts is both fruitless and ill-advised. Sometimes you have to give people the freedom to be wrong and accept the reality that there are those for whom the presentation of reason and evidence is a fruitless offering. The expectation that others can be persuaded or enlightened by a balanced presentation of truth is unrealistic when dealing with those whose insistence on having things done their way is elevated above all other considerations.

To the extent your approach to managing conflict begins with an effort to assign blame to anyone or anything but yourself, the chances of achieving a satisfactory resolution are virtually nil, and in all likelihood you lack the capacity or desire to consider your own contribution to the impasse. A willingness to own our part of the mess is critical to an effective cleanup. Conflict management is possible only when both parties are open to the possibility that their own actions or unrealistic expectations may be an issue.

The introduction of blame also loads up the baggage of defensiveness and the potential addition of an array of emotions that will escalate the friction. When assaulted with blame and accusations it is natural to respond with a vigorous defense of your actions and your character. When this happens, conflict resolution has devolved into verbal arm wrestling between two opponents who are attempting to use the strength of their arguments to gain sufficient leverage to pin their opponent.

There is one word whose use during the process of resolving conflict is almost certain to shift the focus of the conversation from "what is right" to "who is right," and that word is *you*. The introduction of this word during a potentially contentious conversation will almost certainly be perceived by the recipient as an attack against which a timely and appropriate defense must be mustered. This initial response will likely include the word *you* as well and once this word is volleyed back and forth the hope of a successful resolution to the conflict has evaporated. A conversation has now become an argument, and the mutual pursuit of common ground has given way to the need for each individual to dig in and defend their own turf.

"This wouldn't have happened if **you** had only . . ."

"How many times have I told **you** . . ."

"Let's talk about how **you** got us into this mess . . ."

> The introduction of the word *you* in the process of managing conflict can shift the focus away from *what* is right or mutually acceptable to *who* is right and who must win.

The introduction of the word *you* is an emotional trip wire that can quickly shift the focal point of the exchange away from the pursuit of an agreement that will serve mutual interests in favor of a counterproductive exercise in verbal combat. To the extent this process continues, it is very likely that emotion will take a seat at what was once the negotiating table. Not content to take a secondary role, emotion will consume the capacity for either party to relate to one another in a meaningful and productive way. Emotion likes to turn up the volume of what is being said and may even throw in some aggressive body language for good measure. In any case, I don't recall a single instance in which emotion was a productive and useful force for good in the process of attempting to reconcile a conflict. With regard to the probability that emotion will turn up the volume of a disagreement, let me just say that shouting is a pretty good sign that things are moving in the wrong direction.

> A raised voice doesn't strengthen your argument.

In addition to turning up the volume on the argument, emotion loves to play the exaggeration card, and *you* can quickly escalate to *"you never"* or *"you always."* When this happens it is inferred that the recipient of such challenges is to blame for the present situation, and it is also clear that their faults are universal in scope and application. In this moment it can be said that reason has left the building and taken with it any recollection of the actual issue from which the conflict began.

Let's debrief some key points:

A. Be open to the possibility that you bear some responsibility for the conflict. Be willing to admit—verbally, openly, and if necessary, publicly—that you are wrong.

Before launching blame grenades in the direction of the other person, it may be useful to attempt to understand their position. Believe it or not, you may just be wrong. It is also possible that you may not be in possession of all the facts, or that some of what you "know" just may not be so. Don't let your pride and a need to win eclipse your judgment and common sense.

B. Think of the word *you* as an emotional off-ramp that will take you from the highway of productive conversation to the rocky back roads of argument and defensiveness. Making things personal is the strategy of those who lack confidence in their command of the facts and this practice adds nothing productive to the conversation. Not only can it vanquish the possibility of an amicable solution, but also it can result in a total loss of awareness of the original issue that prompted the conflict.

C. When it comes to managing conflict, emotion is not your friend. Emotion consumes reason and is prone to launching words and phrases that inflict the kind of damage that leaves emotional tread marks. For many, the memory of words said to or about them in the heat of an emotional exchange hovers about them like a rain cloud. The introduction of emotion into a conversation whose goal is the mitigation of conflict can result in a weaponized exchange in which the targets are often indiscriminate and the resulting damage can be considerable and, at times, permanent. It is for this reason I recommend that any attempt to resolve a conflict with someone else not be undertaken when either person's feelings on the matter are raw and untended. Wait until the temperature in your hearts and minds has decreased to a level that will permit a useful and productive exchange.

D. If ever there was a situation that requires *engaged listening* it is during the process of attempting to manage conflict. Rehearsing a rebuttal while the other person is talking is a strategy for winning the argument, not one of reconciliation. Make a genuine effort to understand the other person's perspective and how they came to their positions. Taking the time to actively listen as they articulate their position is instructive and respectful and may create an awareness on your part that your conclusions and assumptions are based on erroneous or incomplete information.

E. To the extent your need to be right is overdeveloped, your desire for resolution will be eclipsed by a need to win the day. People who most need to be proven right are the least capable of owning their mistakes and shortcomings. Placing blame is the primary defensive weapon in their interpersonal arsenal, and those given to the blame game are often indiscriminate with regard to who gets wounded in the exchange.

2. I can avoid conflict altogether if I am nice to everybody.
False

Interpersonal conflict is part of the human experience, and there is no one whose life is devoid of interpersonal friction. At a basic level, we are all driven to pursue our own self-interests, and conflict is certain to happen when another person is perceived to be standing between us and our access to that which we desire. We can also find ourselves in the midst of a conflict with no awareness of the nature of our transgression. The new kid at school who unknowingly violates an unwritten cultural norm by sitting at a table in the cafeteria that is claimed as their own by a specific group, or incurring the wrath of a jealous coworker by receiving praise from the boss for a job well done are examples of how we can stumble upon conflict with no effort or intention.

It is inevitable that at some point your personal trajectory will intersect with that of another person in a manner that creates conflict between you, and while it may be your ambition to mind your own business and exercise grace and deference with regard to the indiscretions of others, the time will eventually come when someone else will swerve into your lane in such a manner that the violation can't be ignored or excused. Call it a fundamental aspect of the law of the physics of relationships, but personal conflict will find you at some point in your life and when this happens you must be equipped with the tools necessary to deal with it. I'm reminded of the advice my grandfather gave me on the subject: *"Don't go looking for trouble, but you best know what to do when it comes looking for you."*

> While you may not actively seek conflict, sooner or later it will find you. When it does, it is important to have a strategy and the skills to manage it effectively.

Let's debrief some key points:

A. Conflict is an inevitable component of human interaction, and for each of us, it's not a matter of *if* but *when* we will experience it. Those who fail to grasp this reality will often pursue an attitude of concession and accommodation as strategies to maintain peace. Those who embrace this approach will surrender their credibility in the eyes of others and at a deep level, their self-respect. While few actively seek conflict with others as part of their daily approach to life, conflict has a way of finding its way to all of us. You don't have to actively look for it; it will find its way to you all by itself.

B. "Be a conflict prepper." Given the inevitability of conflict, it is wise to be able to recognize the often-insidious nature of conflict and have a *proactive* strategy for defusing it. To the extent you embrace a personal mission statement of avoiding conflict at all costs, you spend your life running from reality and invite even more conflict from those who perceive you as one who is easy to manipulate. Conflict is like a house fire, and to the extent timely and proactive steps are taken, there is an opportunity to minimize the damage. Running away from the fire for fear of getting burned, however, guarantees the certainty of unnecessary destruction. While the impulse to flee the scene may offer the promise of safety in the near term, to the extent this becomes your strategy for conflict management, you are guaranteeing future destruction. Choosing to run toward a fire is never easy, and those who do must be properly trained in the techniques and procedures necessary for success. Respect is lost and resolution is never achieved when the impulse to run away from difficult conversations is heeded.

3. The best way to deal with conflict is:

E. Talk directly to the person with whom you have the conflict.

In far too many instances, people believe that the path to resolution is to talk *about* the person with whom they are experiencing conflict rather than talking directly *to* them. As such, the decision to engage in conversations with supportive allies is often pursued as a suitable course of action. Talking to your friends affords the opportunity to *transmit* your story to a receptive and sympathetic audience. Beyond the immediate gratification of finding people who share your outrage at the injustices inflicted by the person with whom you *should* be speaking, this behavior does nothing to facilitate an actual resolution. While the counsel of trusted friends can be helpful in difficult situations, my admonition is not to allow this process to become a substitute for an actual engagement with the person with whom you are at odds. Honest self-assessment is required to determine whether your engagement with third parties is motivated by a search for wisdom, or validation. Wisdom searches for *what* is right. Validation seeks a declaration of *who* is right. Wisdom pursues understanding and reasonable solutions. Validation seeks victory and absolution from blame. Wisdom understands that there are times when mutual accountability are necessary. Wisdom and validation have different interpretations of success. Being wise in your approach to conflict resolution means surrendering your need for validation.

> Managing conflict can be like fighting a fire. Proper training and a willingness to go toward the blaze rather than away from it are key aspects of what is required for success.

The possibility of reconciliation can only happen when the individuals involved talk directly to one another. When I say directly, I mean face-to-face. You must run toward the fire if you have any hope of putting it out, and choosing to seek reconciliation from behind an electronic fortress of text messages or social media represents a cowardly retreat. In some cases conversations with the other person may require the presence of an objective third party whose lack of emotional investment in the situation will enable them to guide the conversation in a productive direction.

It bears repeating that unresolved conflict at the end of a flight will find you the next time you fly with the person with whom you have unfinished business. It is for this reason that I strongly recommend that anytime conflict has occurred during the conduct of a flight, the crew actively attempts to resolve it before going their separate ways. While I understand the immediate temptation to put as much distance as possible between yourself and a contentious person once the finality of the destination has been achieved, you must always consider the fact that you may have to fly with this person again. To the extant an unresolved conflict is the punctuation mark at the end of you flight it will be the capital letter that begins your next one. Avoidance is not an effective long-term strategy.

Let's debrief some key points:

A. Seeking the counsel and advice of others when dealing with conflict can be of value but must not be considered a substitute for engagement with the person with whom you *need* to speak. This can only happen in the course of a personal encounter with the other party. Third-party mediators may be necessary at times, and in no case should reconciliation be pursued via text or other similar mediums. This is wimpy and counterproductive.

B. Conflict is like a fire in that the most effective strategy for dealing with it is to go toward it with the proper skills and training necessary to extinguish it. There are certainly risks associated with this strategy, but the choice to run away from the blaze guarantees that it will grow in size and intensity. You can't fight a fire if you are running away from it.

C. Conflict cannot be allowed to have a seat on the flight deck, and you must deal with it before it has a chance to strap in and get comfortable. Don't get off the airplane at the end of a flight if there are conversations that need to occur between you and someone else. Make every attempt to resolve it before you go your separate ways, and be mindful that a failure to do so will guarantee its presence at show time on your next trip with this person. Unresolved conflict is no respecter of duty time limitations and is always rested and ready to go.

4. When resolving conflict with someone, it is best to:

C. Find an appropriate time and location to talk.

When attempting to manage interpersonal conflict, it is important that the process be undertaken at a time and location that are conducive to both privacy and success. Choosing the right time and place to engage with the other person are critical decisions for which wisdom, discretion, and judgment are required. This may mean delaying the conversation until both parties have had a chance to get adequate crew rest, and seeking a location that offers privacy and isolation from those who are not involved in the situation. This is not a party that needs to be well attended in order to be successful.

In the case of a real-time professional conflict for which there are genuine concerns about the operation of the aircraft, the selection of an appropriate time and location becomes a bit more complex. When the actions of one crew member create an imminent threat to safety, the temptation to deal with the issue without first ensuring the safe operation of the aircraft must be resisted. Even in the most emotionally charged moments, strict adherence to the operational hierarchy of *Aviate*, *Navigate*, and *Communicate* must be observed. Flying the aircraft is always the first priority, and only after the operational hazards created by the other person's performance have been addressed should the difficult conversation about the operational foul be initiated. Resolving the operational issue does not mean that all is well between you and there may be personal issues that need to be addressed. Turning from base leg to final on a visual approach or while being vectored for an ILS in low visibility conditions is not an ideal time to initiate these conversations. The best strategy for such engagements is to work them out during a low-workload phase of flight such as the enroute phase of flight or after the aircraft has blocked in. In either case, prudence and judgment should govern your choice of time and location. In the case of professional conflict, the temptation to simply let things slide without a proper debrief is likely to strengthen in proportion to the amount of time that has elapsed since the event in question. When this happens it becomes easier to embrace an "oh well, it all worked out" attitude as justification for avoiding the conversation altogether. In no case in which there has been a professional conflict that created a threat to safety should the crew go their separate ways at the end of the flight without closing the loop.

Regarding the choice of location for the difficult conversations associated with managing conflict, it is important to remember that public engagements can invite the potential for embarrassment, and for this reason great care should be taken to exercise discretion in your selection of a location. No one's interests are served when a private dispute becomes a public drama. Attempting to manage conflict in the presence others greatly diminishes the likelihood of a satisfactory outcome. Some will be drawn to the event like highway motorists slowing down to look at wreckage of an accident, and others will want to flee the scene. Those involved in the resolution process will feel inhibited and exposed and therefore less likely to engage. Just as washing your dirty laundry is not a spectator sport, neither is conflict management. Choosing to pursue reconciliation in a public manner shows a lack of judgment and respect for the other person and is the action of one whose lack of social awareness is appalling.

> Choosing to resolve interpersonal conflict in the presence of others is unwise and disrespectful to the other party.

Those not directly involved in the situation are unnecessary spectators whose presence is both inappropriate and counterproductive. Keep the circle of participants as small and tight as possible, and issue invitations only to those whose presence can help facilitate resolution.

Let's debrief some key points:

A. A critical choice of an appropriate time and location for conflict resolution involves a commitment to refrain from such an engagement when either person's emotions are at high tide. The greater the chasm between the personal or professional expectation and the offending behavior that prompted the conflict, the greater the likelihood of an adverse emotional response. Emotion is more likely to facilitate arguments than the sober and rational engagements required for successful outcomes.

B. While the aspect of choosing a proper time and location requires good judgment, the more important thing to ensure is that the conversation happens at all. Don't use the excuse of *"waiting for the right time"* to become a way of dodging the exchange altogether. Do not retreat when it is necessary to advance. Try as you may to forget about the conflict or downplay the significance of the events that prompted it you must keep these important points in mind: (1) The conflict won't forget you and will reserve the right to influence your next trip with the person with whom you have unfinished business, and (2) the conflict won't simply resolve itself with the passage of time. Bad news doesn't get better with age.

As with any landing, success in managing a conflict begins with a good approach. In the case of taking the action necessary to reconcile the issue, commitment and resolve are required. Before we discuss the specific steps for managing conflict, let's discuss a few points to consider.

1. Dealing with interpersonal conflict is difficult and often unpleasant, and many are inclined to go to great lengths to avoid the process. Denying the existence of a problem altogether, avoiding the contact with the other person,

or embracing a posture of concession at any cost in the pursuit of peace are common strategies that will erode the foundations of trust upon which relationships are built. The stakes in aviation are such that these strategies of denial and avoidance cannot be entertained. Safety can never be sacrificed in the pursuit of a desire to avoid difficulty.

2. Conflict management takes courage. In the moment, the voice of the easy way is strong and will encourage you to say nothing and allow time to resolve the problem. The logic of the easy way seems appealing, but it is lying to you. Pretending something isn't broken doesn't make it so, and hope is not an effective repair manual. In the case of unresolved conflict, ignorance is not bliss, and willful denial is self-deception. Unresolved conflict is an open wound that must be treated with skillful and timely attention and not allowed to fester as a result of neglect.

3. Conflict management is the responsibility of every member of the crew. Safety is everybody's business, and no one gets a pass from these uncomfortable engagements by using the excuse that it's the other person's responsibility to take the first step. While it may in fact be the case that the other person should take the initiative to address the issue between you, their failure to do so doesn't give you a pass. Conversation is a two-way street and in the case of conflict management both parties share the same pavement.

NOTE: Having the last word or *"telling the other person a thing or two"* should not be confused with satisfactory conflict management.

D. It's never helpful to ascribe motive to the actions and thoughts of another: *"You're only saying/doing this because* _____." To proclaim with certainty that you know the thoughts and motivations of another is an act of rendering judgment. Such accusations reflect the disposition of a condescending mind reader who seems motivated by a desire to reframe the argument in a manner that is consistent with their predetermined conclusions or beliefs. This is a strategy for establishing a home-field advantage in pursuit of a victory rather than the creation of a platform upon which mutual understanding can be established. Whenever you have doubts about someone's motives, it's always better to begin your investigation with questions rather than accusatory proclamations.

While the principles associated with conflict management have broad application to all aspects of life, their application is especially critical for those in positions of leadership. With regard to the dynamics of the flight deck, it must be said that captains who refuse to take the initiative to manage conflict are sacrificing not only flight safety but also the respect of those under their command. Doing nothing is perceived as weakness, and the deafening silence of those who are disappointed or disenchanted as a result of your inaction will come at a cost you may never fully realize and from which you may not recover. No one respects a coward, and the climate of command you cultivate as a result of your unwillingness to engage in the necessary conversations expected of you will be characterized by a perception of weakness. No one wants to follow a weak leader, and an unwillingness to engage will tarnish the luster of your stripes.

> A captain unwilling to manage conflict is willing to surrender the respect of the crew. A crew respects a captain who goes toward a fire more than one who runs away from it.

Conflict Management Strategies

Here are some helpful strategies for managing conflict. This model is comprised of three steps, each of which has specific words of instruction. Each step begins with a verb, which means it requires action on your part. The most important aspect of this process is the one that isn't mentioned specifically—the need to be *proactive*. Flight safety demands that you move *toward* the problem *not* away from it.

I've distilled this process down to these three steps, each of which has three distinct components that will be explained in some detail. This is a straightforward outline comprised of three simple tasks: **Ask 3, Make 3, Do 3**

1. Ask 3 questions of yourself.
2. Make 3 statements.
3. Do 3 things.

1. Ask 3 questions of yourself. *Make an accurate diagnosis before prescribing treatment.* This step is critical to ensuring that you have a clear understanding of the nature of the problem. Trying to resolve a situation before having a firm grasp of the facts is often fueled by emotion or the impulse to appear decisive, and it is one that must be resisted. This approach is likely to result in the creation of additional conflicts, and for this reason it is always best to think of yourself first as a detective. The best sleuths engage in a process of asking questions and gathering evidence before identifying suspects and pressing charges.

It is often the case that our understanding of a situation that we observe when we walk into a room can lead us to conclusions that may or may not be based on a full set of facts. As the saying goes, there is often "more to the story than meets the eye," and one who wants to prescribe a solution to a problem must first endeavor to determine an accurate diagnosis.

> It is important to ask questions to diagnose the basis of a conflict before writing a prescription for its resolution. Always diagnose before you prescribe.

Here are three important questions to ask yourself:

A. What are my expectations? What exactly do I expect in this situation? This could refer to the standard you expect regarding personal appearance and demeanor, or to their performance in the execution of their professional duties. It is a necessary question when what you are witnessing is contrary to what you would expect in this particular situation. When there is a disconnect between expectations and real-life experience it's a good idea to try to consider the possibility that there is a reason beyond the obvious that is prompting the other person's behavior.

B. What are the other person's expectations? When it becomes clear that you and the other person have different expectations with regard to personal or professional conduct it is a good idea to compare and evaluate your differences. Give the other person the benefit of the doubt before drawing conclusions and be mindful of the fact that it's possible that you are making assumptions based on an incomplete set of facts. Ask nonaccusatory questions in an attempt to gain clarification.

For example, if a member of your crew with whom you have never flown shows up late to afford them the opportunity to give an account of their tardiness before launching into a lecture about the values of punctuality and responsibility. While it may prove to be the case that such a lesson is entirely necessary and appropriate for the situation, there is also the possibility that their tardiness is the result of something beyond their control. At least be open to the consideration of other variables in the equation before you race to conclusions. Conflict resolution is a difficult process, and in such situations, it is absolutely critical to have all the facts possible at your disposal before engaging in an attempt at reconciliation. All of us can recall the cringe-worthy moments when we attempted to resolve a dispute prior to having a clear understanding of all the pertinent facts. Things get unnecessarily messy and complicated when the problem you are attempting to solve is not the one that needs attention. Be a good detective, and try to have all the evidence before solving the case.

> The standards you apply to yourself are the same ones you will apply to others. To the extent they are unrealistic, your expectations of others will also be.

C. What is the basis for my expectation? Additional clarity to the previous question can be found by asking yourself if the basis for your expectation is objective or subjective. Let's look at the difference between each.

- **Objective expectations.** The behavior in question is contrary to guidance set forth in official publications such as company SOP or FAA regs. If the action is clearly in violation of the expectations outlined in official policies or procedures, the decision to engage is an easy one.

- **Subjective expectations.** In these instances, it is necessary to consider the fact that while a particular action is contrary to what you expect, it does not violate established organizational guidelines. It could be that you just have to accept the fact that this individual has a different method or technique for accomplishing a particular task and your differences are rooted in individual preferences more than violations of established policy. Allow for the possibility that while the other person's conduct may be contrary to your preferred practices, it is not beyond established boundaries. Consider the possibility that your specific rules for life may be more stringent than those embraced by others, and exercise great care against elevating a personal preference to that of a standard to which others must aspire.

Such occasions offer the opportunity to evaluate the reasons for our insistence on adherence to our specific and unwritten codes of conduct and consider the prudence of surrendering our insistence on having things done our way. Even the things that don't matter. Especially the things that don't matter. Here are some important self-awareness questions to ask during this part of the **Ask 3** process.

- Is it possible that you are motivated by a strong dislike for the other person that predisposes you to reject their preferences?
- Do you "need" to find something wrong with their appearance, conduct, or performance as a way to elevate your own status and position?
- Is your commitment to your own method of doing things such that you are threatened by the possibility that another person's may be superior?

2. Make 3 Statements. *Engage with tact and purpose.*

A. Own the problem with an "I" statement. Beginning the process of engagement with an "I" statement is a way of taking initiative in a manner that won't invite a defensive response. *"I'm not comfortable with this,"* or *"I'm not sure what's going on,"* are statements that create the impression that you are the one who is confused and in need of clarification, and neither statement is likely to be perceived by the other person as a personal challenge.

This gives the other person a feeling of leverage, as it puts them in the position to enlighten you with things known only to them. Knowledge is power, and to the extent you put the other person in a position of being able to tell you things that are known only by them, you are providing them the opportunity to share their expectations in a manner that is more likely to promote clarity than one that puts them in a position to defend themselves.

B. State the problem as you see it. Follow the "I" statement with a clear and concise description of the issue that is the basis of your concern. Make your remarks factual, and avoid any implication of wrong-doing. Remember the four "Be's" here. You are making the case for your objection to actions that are contrary to your expectations in this particular situation, and there can be no margin for of ambiguity or confusion regarding your concern. If your objection pertains to the operation of the aircraft, a reference to official sources that provide evidence to support your concern is helpful. References to guidelines from the Flight Ops Manual, FARs, or aircraft operating limitations are examples of objective standards of which both parties are aware whose authority they acknowledge. Such references offer facts that cannot be disputed and violations are not a matter of one person's opinion over the other. In circumstances in which the other individual's behavior is not altered by the presentation of this type of objective evidence, the use of "hammer" words may be necessary. "Hammer" words are meant to get someone's attention, and the imagery here is meant to suggest the need to hit them hard with reminders of the implications of their continued deviation. Reminding a captain that a particular course of action is "unsafe" or "illegal" are examples of "hammer" words that can be effective in arousing them from their obstinate slumber.

C. Prescribe a solution. This is the step that is most often overlooked. Humans are quite adept when it comes to stating problems, and for some, there is often a sense of validation or satisfaction that is felt as a result of having done so. We are given to talking about what is wrong and what needs to be done about it and feel as though such comments equate to productive engagement and problem solving. We reason that negative outcomes that arise after our proclamations are no longer our fault or responsibility and when misfortune occurs we can say with full confidence, *"I tried to tell you."* Being content to simply identify a problem and believe that you have contributed to a satisfactory resolution is another example of the easy way out. In point of fact, you have accomplished little more than sounding like someone who wants to complain to everyone about what is wrong. This practice requires neither courage nor skill and does nothing to resolve the problem. Instead, have a possible solution in mind before bringing the problem to the other person's attention. This is the action of one who is committed to resolving the issue rather than one whose mission is to ensure that others are aware of their dissatisfaction. Pointing out problems with no recommendations for solutions makes you sound like a critic rather than a problem solver, and the former isn't particularly adept at conflict resolution. Right though you may be with your facts, the bigger truth is that even the most patient among us grow weary of criticism as a communication strategy. Proposing a solution gives the other person options to consider not only increases the likelihood of a satisfactory outcome but may also offer the other person the opportunity to save face. When proposing a solution, I strongly recommend the use of "we" language. The solution you are offering is a recommendation of a course of action that involves the entire crew as opposed to a focused opinion regarding a specific action that one individual should undertake. The former advocates for a particular course of action to be undertaken collectively, while the latter singles out a particular as the one who is uniquely responsible for a particular outcome. *"I think you should divert to the alternate,"* is far less effective than saying, *"Why don't we divert to our alternate?"* Such a small and subtle distinction can make a big difference in a stressful and potentially emotional situation.

3. *Do 3* Things. *Know when to Stop, Adapt, and Press*

A. **Stop talking.** Once you've made your case and presented the evidence that supports your concern, there comes a moment when it's necessary for you to stop talking and allow the other person the opportunity to respond. In this case, it's critical that you actively listen to what they have to say. They have listened to your concerns and recommendations, and now it's time to afford them equal respect by returning the courtesy. As Mark Twain said, *"Never miss an opportunity to shut up."* In this moment, you must be open to the possibility that there are factors in the equation for which you have not given adequate consideration, and for that reason your assumptions or conclusions may be at odds with the facts. This is the time for *engaged listening* and an open mind that is more committed to what is true than to being right.

B. **Adapt as necessary.** Be open to the idea that the other person's conduct or performance is entirely appropriate for the situation. You may be wrong and they may be right. It may also be the case that their reasoning or expectations are based on things you haven't considered or of which you are unaware and, as such, are perfectly sound and reasonable. If you are the junior member of the crew, remember that the captain's decisions are final. You may not like or agree with the course of action that is being undertaken, but unless it is unsafe or unlawful the ultimate decision rests with the one who wears the most stripes.

C. Press for closure. There are both immediate and long-term aspects of this step. The immediate concern is for the presentation of a clear course of action that addresses the concerns of all. Pressing for closure in the short term may involve decisions that resolve immediate concerns. If short-term problems have been resolved without closure on the bigger issues it may be necessary to return to the "I" portion of the process in an attempt to fully close the loop. Addressing an immediate concern does not always mean that the conflict has been fully resolved.

In some cases, the decision to "finish this later" may be appropriate but should not be allowed to be used as an excuse to allow later to become never. Be prepared to continue with the same momentum you created when you took the initiative to pursue resolution and use the occasion of the post-flight debrief to finish what you started. Resolve your differences now rather than postponing them until later. Refuse to let interpersonal conflict take command of your flight deck. Flight safety demands that it be managed and a failure to do so is an act of operational negligence.

CREW SITUATIONAL AWARENESS

Chapter 11

Be Operationally Aware

Know How to Manage Threats to Safety

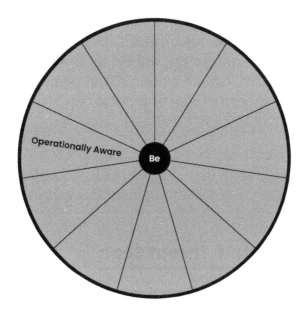

In chapter 1 we introduced the critical link between the Crew Envelope and flight safety and referred to CRM skills as the primary line of defense against threats to safety. As you recall, a threat to safety is defined as any operational event or situation that increases the potential for human error, and the best defense against them is a proactive commitment to the principles outlined in the subsequent chapters.

Given the complexities of the aviation system, maintaining Crew SA is a dynamic and ongoing process. Furthermore, it can be said that Crew SA is a team rather than an individual sport in the sense that what is known and understood about a situation is useful only to the extent it is known equally by all. As such, it is for this reason that I have added the word *Crew* to the conventional term *Situational Awareness*. If only one member of the crew is aware of a critical piece of the operational puzzle, its value is limited if this information is not shared by all. I call this Solo SA, and to the extent it exists on a flight deck in which the free and open exchange of information is lacking, safety dividends are less likely to materialize. Furthermore, when the flight is operated in the shadow of unresolved conflict or leadership that is exercised in a manner that discourages input, Crew SA will be undermined to the point that flight safety will be jeopardized. The skewed sense of reality that results when critical pieces of information are not equally shared invites bad decisions.

> The operational clarity necessary for Crew SA is possible only when everyone on the flight deck has equal access to the pieces of the operational puzzle.

Develop an Active Threat Scan

Crew SA is critical to managing threats to safety. Managing a threat means you are limiting its adverse impact on the operation and reducing the opportunity for error or dealing with mistakes that do occur in a timely manner. An effective means of achieving these objectives is with the development of an effective *Threat Scan*. Use this image of a radar scope to imagine a practical approach to developing such a practice. The three "blips" on the screen represent specific targets that must be monitored as you look for indications that things are not as they should be. I've identified these targets according to three categories - **P**eople, **R**esources, and **E**xpectations, or **PRE**. These are specific things that can be observed by each member of the crew and an effective *Threat Scan* requires constant monitoring of all three. Think of **PRE** as an operational prefix that will be applied to every phase of flights from preflight to block-in. Just as with radar, active scanning is essential to identify potential threats that require mitigation strategies to limit their impact on operational safety. Your *Threat Scan* should look for things that are not as they ought to be in these particular areas and will serve as your brain's early warning system as it alerts you to the need for action.

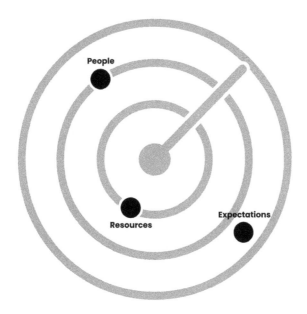

> A proper threat scan is focused on looking for things that are not as they should be. Look for what doesn't fit, and don't allow experience to negate your curiosity.

Let's discuss each of these "blips" in some detail.

People—*Are the individuals with whom you are operating fully prepared to function at their highest performance? Are you?* Anyone for whom this question cannot be answered in the affirmative is a potential threat to safety and this includes the person who looks back at you in the mirror. While the team formation process should include an exchange that offers each crew member the opportunity to attest to their preparation, the question of fitness for duty should be resolved on an individual basis before you show up to fly. Monitor others for signs that their readiness is compromised by such things as stress or fatigue, and monitor yourself as well.

It is worth repeating that a crew is only as strong as its individual members and the responsibility for a thorough *Preflight Self-Check* is shared equally. Bringing anything less than your best to the flight is an act of disrespect toward your crew.

> "Good enough" is neither good nor enough. Aspire to a higher standard or find another profession.

The notion of scanning yourself for the presence of potential threats requires an honest assessment of your own level of proficiency and preparation as well as your attitude and motivation. Preparation and proficiency fuel your ability to operate, while attitude and motivation determine your willingness to give your best. The first two are objective metrics while the latter are subjective influences that others may see before you do. Here are some examples of "self-threats," personal issues that may impair your performance.

Interpersonal conflict—If you are scheduled to fly with someone with whom you have unresolved conflict how will this issue impact your ability, or desire, to operate cooperatively and professionally? What strategies will you employ to ensure that your ability to work as a team is not jeopardized?

Stress and fatigue—We will discuss these issues in greater detail later in this chapter, but for now suffice it to say that stress and fatigue will degrade your technical proficiency and mental engagement and their influence can render you a walking, talking, threat to safety. Given our inability to objectively assess our own levels of impairment from these influences, it is likely that others will recognize the warning signs in you before you will see them in yourself.

Resources—*Is any of the equipment required for this flight operating at less than full capacity? Are there technical components unique to this series of aircraft with which I lack familiarity or recent experience?* This is a broad category that includes the systems aboard your aircraft and the variations that may exist within your fleet or the vast array of equipment such as approach lights and navigation aids that are critical to the operation. To the extent any of these resources are partially or completely out of service, the complexity of operations will increase and with it a greater likelihood for error.

In some instances awareness of inoperative systems or equipment can be determined in advance of your flight and in these situations you have the luxury of reviewing guidelines that address the issue prior to strapping in. It's always easier to develop and brief strategies to manage threats to safety while you're sitting still. The challenge becomes more complicated when equipment failures are encountered while the aircraft is moving. It is in these situations that your leadership and CRM skills are most tested and required.

> The challenge of managing threats to safety is magnified when the aircraft is moving.

Expectations—*Are others performing their duties as expected? Is the aircraft being flown in accordance with established policy and procedural guidelines? Are we operating in a manner that is contrary to what was briefed?* This category requires an ongoing comparison of what *is* happening with what you *thought would* happen. As stated in the previous chapter, these expectations can be personal or professional and are evaluated from the moment you shake hands with the person with whom you are flying. As you interact, you develop a sense of what it will be like to fly with this person and what you can expect based on such things as their level of experience, knowledge, demeanor, and attention to important details. As you review and discuss the weather and flight plan you develop an expectation of how the flight will proceed and adjustments that may be necessary along the way. There is also the expectation that both of you are skilled, knowledgeable, and equally committed to operating in accordance with SOP.

There is an old saying that no battle plan ever survives the first shot, and this adage certainly applies to the arena of aviation. In over forty years of flying, I can't recall a single instance in which everything that happened on the flight was perfectly aligned with what was planned and expected when I reported for duty. In some cases, the individuals with whom I was operating didn't meet my personal or professional expectations and in other instances the introduction of operational surprises required adaptation to new realities. The most challenging flights were those in which both types of expectations were violated.

A critical component of an effective *Threat Scan* includes a commitment to address the anomalies on your screen in a timely manner. Never assume that just because you are aware of the presence of a threat to safety that everyone else sees it also. This often happens when you notice something so obvious that it can't possibly be missed by others, and their apparent lack of concern convinces you that you are overstating the threat. The silence of others in the midst of something you perceive to be a big deal has a way of casting doubt on your own judgment and can easily result in silence on your part. This is especially the case when a junior FO is paired with a senior captain. There is a natural reluctance on the part of the FO to verbalize concerns that don't capture the attention of a captain who is perceived to be all-knowing and all-seeing, and to the extent the captain isn't making a big deal of it, the FO will be less inclined to say what needs to be said. In the mind of the FO, verbalizing a concern that may turn out to be much ado about nothing invites the possibility of embarrassment and a loss of respect from the captain. It's always better to accept these potential outcomes than risk the regret of not having spoken up when you should have. All of us have moments in which we have exposed ourselves to ridicule by expressing a concern that turned out to be a nonissue. While those moments make for funny stories to tell about yourself, they don't haunt you like the remembrances of the times you should have spoken up but chose the "safe" way of silence instead.

Threats to safety do not respect rank or experience and are not subject to the social consequences of embarrassment. Nothing is gained by keeping your doubts to yourself, and it may well turn out that your concerns are unfounded. Don't let the fear of looking foolish undermine the effectiveness of your threat scan. It bears repeating the reminder from a previous chapter that embarrassment has never been cited as a causal factor in an accident, but a failure to speak up in a timely manner to address an operational concern has been the downfall of many.

> Your threat radar is of limited value if you don't let others know what's on your screen. Never assume that everyone's radar is painting the same threats.

To the extent you and your fellow crew members have a robust and ongoing *Threat Scan*, you are engaging in a process known as *Threat and Error Management (TEM)*. This is an operational philosophy whose focus underscores the importance of monitoring the **PRE** targets on your screen. Three principal elements of TEM are *threat awareness, error detection,* and *error correction.* Let's examine each in some detail.

1. Threat Awareness. *Brief to build Crew SA.* As we have discussed, threats to safety elevate operational risk and increase the potential for error. Threat awareness involves the process of ensuring that Solo SA becomes Crew SA. Threat awareness requires a solid communication loop, and its strength is established during the team formation process. It is during this exchange that the operational climate is established and expectations are assessed and defined. Briefings that are organized and thorough are a verbal investment in safety for which enhanced Crew SA and sound decision-making are the dividends. Being organized is the practice of attention to important details and thoroughness includes a careful discussion of strategies to counter threats to safety.

A. Proper threat awareness is crew awareness and it begins with a statement on the part of the captain of the intention to operate in accordance with SOP and the expectation that others will speak up in a timely manner to identify threats to safety.

B. These briefings activate the crew's *Threat Scan*, and this prompts everyone to incorporate the future tense into their operational mindset. Threat awareness demands that your brain always moves faster than the aircraft, and a properly developed *Threat Scan* can divide its attention between the present and the future. Shared awareness of what is happening right now is only part of the equation, and attention must be paid to what may happen as a result of current action or inaction. What you do or fail to do in the moment may cause you problems at a later point in the flight, and the ability to balance present actions with future implications is a key element of Crew SA. Never let the aircraft take you somewhere your brain hasn't already considered. Always think and plan forward. That's where the aircraft is going.

> **Brief to build Crew SA.** Organized and thorough briefings are essential for building Crew SA.

2. Error Detection. *Monitor to maintain Crew* SA. Monitoring is the skill by which crews can recognize not only threats to safety but also the errors that occur during the flight. The importance of monitoring as a crew responsibility is underscored by the fact that it is identified as a flight crew job description in both company Flight Ops Manuals and the FARs"

FAR 121.544 Pilot Monitoring.

Each pilot who is seated at the pilot controls of the aircraft, while not flying the aircraft, must accomplish pilot monitoring duties as appropriate in accordance with the certificate holder's procedures contained in the manual required by § 121.133 of this part.

This regulation officially establishes the position of *Pilot Monitoring (PM)*, and by virtue of the reference to FAR 121.133 delegates the responsibility to each carrier to establish specific guidelines for PM duties and responsibilities.

Adequate monitoring of the aircraft and the activities of other crew members requires a continuous posture of active mental engagement. You can expect to spend half of your time on the flight deck in the role of PM and must apply yourself to the practice of monitoring with the same dedication you give to the execution of your duties as the *Pilot Flying* (PF). Monitoring is a proactive process that seeks to identify deviations from personal and operational expectations and is critical to ensuring that Crew SA is maintained. The challenge for the PM is to resist the temptation to allow past success to foster a diminished level of vigilance. During your PM legs think of yourself as being on guard duty. When the guard has little or no expectation of the presence of threats to the safety of the group, the possibility of falling asleep while on duty is elevated. Likewise, long periods of uneventful flying can foster the operational slumber known as complaency, and to the extent it finds a comfortable home on your flight deck your threat radar is likely to be more ornamental than operational.

It is the PM who is best equipped for the role of identifying threats in a timely manner and upon whom the PF must rely during periods when the demands of flying the aircraft consume his or her attention. The amount of focus necessary to fly the aircraft with skill and precision is such that the PF will not have the mental capacity to identify and manage threats that are obvious to the PM. This is especially the case during high workload phases of flight such as departure or arrival. For this reason, the PF may not see things that the PM can't miss. During the legs on which I was the PM, I would consider the PF to be operationally limited during these phases of flight and would think of myself as having the responsibility of scanning for both of us.

> **Monitor to maintain Crew SA.** Your role as PM is that of primary safety observer, and requires a posture of active mental engagement.

3. Error Management. *Connect to correct errors and restore Crew SA.* Proactive verbal engagement is essential for correcting crew errors. It is for this reason that I like to refer to these conversations as *crew glue*, as they are essential to maintaining the integrity of the shared mental model necessary to detect and correct errors.

> **Connect to correct errors.** Safety demands proactive engagement to correct errors.

This is the essence of TEM as described in a few short statements.

Briefing outlines the gameplan for TEM and set the tone for its application.

Monitoring ensures that TEM is proactive and ongoing.

Connecting takes action to correct errors and minimize their impact on the operation.

It's just that simple. Don't let its simplicity fool you into thinking of TEM as a nice-to-know slogan. Instead, think of it as a strategy that establishes operational guardrails. Make TEM not just something you *know* to be important, but an operating philosophy that describes what you *believe* to be necessary for safe operations.

SA Warning Lights

Data collected from years of accident investigations and voluntary reporting programs has identified specific warning signs that point to a loss of SA on the flight deck. Just as a flashing light on your instrument panel draws your attention to the need for prompt corrective action, the same response must be given to the presence of an SA warning light. The failure to respond in a timely manner can result in the introduction of additional warning lights as your SA becomes further degraded. To the extent you have two flashing SA warning lights for which corrective action is not being taken, you are at greater risk for a flight violation. Data collected over the years from accidents in which a loss of SA figured into the causality of the mishap has revealed that in most cases at least four SA warning lights were active on the flight deck.

The presence of an SA warning light signals a compromised level of operational awareness that increases the likelihood of error. In a general sense, these lights represent the introduction of a variable that has caused the crew to lose sight of the big picture because of distraction, confusion, or a single-minded focus on a specific item to the exclusion of other factors. SA warning lights introduce additional complexities to the operation and a failure to address them in a timely manner threatens flight safety. The first response to awareness of an SA warning light is to make sure that its presence is known to everyone on the flight deck. This involves sharing the details of what you are seeing, not seeing, or don't understand that are the basis of your concern. Think of this as an emergency procedure whose action items are outlined in the third step of TEM. The presence of even one SA warning light requires a proactive response.

SA warning lights are mental signals that alert your brain to the fact that a significant gap exists between what is happening and what should be happening. In many cases, the first indication of a flashing SA warning light is the feeling that something *doesn't look right* or *doesn't feel right*. These sensations are commonly referenced together and referred to as DLR/DFR moments. We've all experienced a DLR/DFR moment in life when there was a person, place, or situation about which we were uneasy for reasons that weren't easy to identify or explain. There was *just something about it* that made you uneasy or uncertain. In these moments our innate tendency is to override our curiosity with hopeful explanations that pacify our concerns or seek an exit strategy that distances us from the uncomfortable situation altogether. During a DLR/DFR moment our curiosity and desire for an assurance that everything is and will be OK can often wrestle for supremacy as we consider our response. In situations in which the threat is not obvious we are more given to the latter pursuit and will look for signs that reinforce our desire for confirmation that nothing is amiss. In a dynamic and complex arena such as aviation in which threats to safety are magnified by inattention or neglect, such wishful thinking cannot be indulged. Don't throw cold water on your curiosity during DLR/DFR moments that often accompany flashing SA warning lights. Allow it full reign and follow it with the diligence of a bloodhound.

DLR/DFR moments are a call to action for your curiosity to engage with your *Threat Scan* in a thorough inventory to ensure that your operational house is in order. The DLR/DFR sensation should prompt investigation and must not be pacified by dismissive explanations that seek to offer assurance that *"it's probably nothing."*

> A DLR/DFR moment is a tap on the shoulder that suggests that something is not as it should be. Allow it stimulate rather than stifle your operational curiosity.

Here are the common warning lights that will alert you to the SA need for timely and corrective action.

1. Ambiguity/confusion
2. Not communicating
3. Fatigue
4. Preoccupation/distraction
5. Rushing
6. Willful violation of SOP
7. Interrupted checklist or habit pattern
8. Not addressing discrepancies
9. Failure to set or meet targets

1. Ambiguity/Confusion. This warning light begins to flash when you receive conflicting information from two trusted sources. If your flight director tells you that you are above the glideslope but the PAPI says you are too low, ambiguity and confusion are present as you attempt to reconcile the disparity. Both are reliable sources of information, and I have come to expect them to be in agreement during this phase of the flight, but in this instance they are telling different stories. Which is fact and which is fiction?

The answer to this question requires a timely response as the aircraft is descending into uncertainty. In a situation like this, it's best to begin your detective work with questions such as: *"Did we enter the proper ILS frequency?"* and, *"Are we lined up on the correct runway?"* While the answers to such questions may resolve the flashing SA warning light, this kind of investigative work must not eclipse your awareness of the fact that you are descending toward the ground. These are situations in which it is tempting to sacrifice the top priority of flying the aircraft safely in favor of the immediate desire to reconcile the disparity. In a low-altitude situation like this in which the ambiguity cannot be reconciled quickly, revert to your *Aviate, Navigate, Communicate* hierarchy of priorities. This means climbing the aircraft to a safe altitude and then ensuring that one person is flying while the other seeks to reconcile the disparity.

Ambiguity and confusion can also result from the uncertainty associated with vertigo and visual illusions associated with "black hole" conditions. Black hole approaches are those flown for an extended distance over dark and featureless terrain to runways located in areas in which the absence of surrounding lights plays tricks on your depth perception. In these situations, it is common to experience the sensation of being "too high" when you are below the prescribed glide path. In these instances, what you *know* from the PAPI is at odds with what you *believe* and numerous accidents have occurred when pilots increased their descent rate in such situations and impacted the ground well short of the runway. When this sensation of feeling like you are too high is contradicted by PAPI lights that show you to be too low the SA light is flashing. In the case of vertigo, the information from your brain is contradicted by what your instruments are telling you and you may have the sensation of being in a turn while your attitude gyro says you are flying straight and level. in this situation your instruments will tell a story that differs from the one being told by your senses, and ambiguity and confusion can rule the moment as you attempt to discern which is the more reliable source. *Which is right, what I feel or what I'm being told by a reliable external source?*

NOTE: In instrument conditions always consider your instruments to be more reliable than your senses. Flight instruments are regularly maintained and calibrated to exacting standards, while your senses are not. One reflects objective reality while the other offers a sensory-driven assessment of the situation. One is what you *know,* and the other promotes what you *feel.* In these situations, the safest course of action is to go with what you know.

2. Not communicating. Along with ambiguity and confusion, this SA warning light connects the dots between communication and Crew SA. This SA warning light refers not only to long periods of silence that may accompany a DLR/DFR moment but also includes flight deck conversations whose deviation from the four "Be's" (Be: precise, succinct, timely, acknowledged) may invite ambiguity or confusion. A failure to share feelings of operational ambiguity or confusion is an example of how one SA warning light can easily become two.

3. Fatigue. While there are significant cultural and national differences among nations and people groups throughout the world, in the matter of sleep, there is great uniformity with regard to our common need for it and the degree to which our performance is degraded when we are deprived of it. The fatigue SA warning light is one for which the person most affected is often the least qualified and equipped to assess its presence and influence, and for this reason the warning signs of its introduction to your flight deck must be assessed as part of your **PRE** threat scan.

Let's being with a discussion of three causes of fatigue. Your familiarity with these factors will establish an objective baseline from which an accurate performance and cognitive assessment can be conducted:

A. **Sleep loss**
B. **Continuous hours of wakefulness**
C. **Disruption to your circadian cycle**

A. Sleep loss. The average adult needs an average of eight hours of sleep in each twenty-four-hour period. The use of the word *average* is intentional, as there are some who require a bit more or less sleep on a daily basis. For purposes of this discussion we will use 8 hours as our baseline. Another variable in this equation is the fact that the amount of sleep the human body requires can vary as a function of age. Babies require more sleep during critical developmental stages, and this physiological need tends to be reduced as a function of the aging process.

Pay attention to your body and its need for sleep. To the extent your body doesn't get its desired amount, you are experiencing sleep loss. While isolated occurrences of sleep loss will simply result in the sensation of being tired, when it becomes a chronic issue, you are more apt to become fatigued. Sleep loss is cumulative, and when you lose 1.5 hours of sleep for five nights in a row, you have lost the equivalent of a whole night's sleep. When this happens you are said to be experiencing "sleep debt." Your body has reached the shutdown and reboot phase of its operation and will demand the sleep it is owed. Interestingly, when your body cashes in on its sleep debt it doesn't sleep for a whole extra day to make up for lost time, but instead goes to a deeper stage of sleep more quickly than usual and stays there for a longer period of time. The body is an amazing machine, and sleep is essential for its self-maintenance.

The ability to develop consistent sleep patterns can be a significant challenge in aviation, and this difficulty is compounded by factors such as crossing multiple time zones and operations conducted on the "back side of the clock." The good news is that the need for eight hours in a twenty-four-hour period doesn't have to be satisfied in one period. If a single eight-hour sleep session is not possible multiple sessions that allow you to get a total of 8 hours is the next best thing.

> Make sleep a priority on your layovers, and monitor the amount you are able to get on a daily basis. Make it your goal to get as close as possible to eight hours of sleep in each twenty-four-hour period.

B. Continuous hours of wakefulness. This refers to the amount of time that has elapsed since you awoke from your last sleep period. The human body is a finely designed machine, and like any other, it has performance limitations that must be heeded to ensure optimal performance. The human machine begins to operate at diminished capacity once it has been awake for twelve continuous hours, and this decline becomes more pronounced with time. Once this limitation is exceeded, performance and cognitive ability deteriorate, and what is unique about the human body is the unwillingness of its owner and operator to acknowledge when their personal envelope has been breached. Much like a person who has been drinking, people who have been awake for longer periods of time are given to overestimating their ability to deal with the cognitive impairment and performance degradation that result from fatigue. While you may think that the mention of cognitive impairment and the consumption of alcohol are random additions to a discussion of fatigue, there are notable similarities between the two. A person who has been awake for an extended period of time demonstrates a degree of impairment that is consistent with the effects one experiences when they have had too much to drink. Here are some of the warning signs of brought on by the effects of alcohol or fatigue:

- Diminished near-term memory
- Loss of sustained focus
- Involuntary head bobbing
- Persistent yawning
- Random or poorly organized thoughts
- No desire to communicate
- Degraded performance of routine procedures

Given each person's inability to accurately recognize and assess degraded performance or cognitive deficiencies brought on by fatigue, it is absolutely essential for each member of the crew to monitor the other for the presence of warning signs. The presence of one of these indicators by itself may not be definitive proof of fatigue but should be evaluated in context with other factors such as cumulative sleep loss and hours of continuous wakefulness. When you find yourself on the wrong side of these numbers, don't try to hide it—especially from your crew. They are counting on you to be as rested and ready as possible, and to the extent you try to present yourself as "feeling fine" when you have been awake for fifteen hours, you are lying to them and yourself. In this moment, you are a threat to safety.

> Performance and cognitive abilities begin to decline once you've been awake for twelve continuous hours. Monitor yourself and your crew for the warning signs of impairment.

Here are some performance limitations that define the physiological boundaries of your personal envelope. Commit them to memory and show them the same respect you demonstrate for aircraft limitations.

- Signs of cognitive impairment begin to emerge after twelve hours of continuous wakefulness.

- A person who has been awake for seventeen continuous hours can experience the same level of cognitive impairment as someone whose blood alcohol concentration (BAC) is .05 percent.

- A person who has been awake for twenty-four continuous hours is likely to experience a level of impairment consistent with someone whose BAC is .10 percent.

- NOTE: A BAC of .10 percent is the legal standard for intoxication.

C. Disruption of your Circadian cycle. The Circadian cycle is your body's internal clock that manages and regulates critical bodily functions. This biological scheduler is naturally programmed to operate in sync with the day/night cycle of life. Your Circadian clock is comprised of about twenty thousand nerve cells (neurons) that form a structure called the suprachiasmatic nucleus, or SCN, which is located in a part of the brain called the hypothalamus. The SCN receives direct input from the eyes and is predisposed to signal the body to be alert and productive when daylight is the primary stimulus and will begin the process of slowing down in preparation for a period of sleep when daylight gives way to darkness. Your body uses this Circadian cycle to regulate physiological functions such as body temperature and food digestion, and constant disruptions of this cycle have been linked to chronic health conditions such as obesity, diabetes, depression, bipolar disorder, and sleep disorders. This physiological master clock represents a simple design that has worked in concert with the natural and recurring day/night cycle of everyday life for centuries. With the introduction of electricity and indoor lighting came the ability for tasks once performed during daylight hours to be completed at any time, and with this change came the practice of sacrificing natural sleep cycles in favor of those that offered the opportunity for greater profit and productivity. Fast-forward to the present day, and ours is a 24/7 world in which productivity and sleep are no longer managed in accordance with the natural order of things but in alignment with schedules of our own creation. While the body's regulatory design has not changed, the demands now placed upon it are often at odds with its best interests.

Aviation scheduling and the design of our Circadian clock are often on less-than-friendly and to the extent they operate as foes, fatigue will be a chronic issue within any organization. Starting your duty day at 0100 when your body is accustomed to being asleep, or attempting to get crew rest during the time of day when the presence of daylight tells your body it is time to be up and around can present significant challenges. Finding a satisfactory balance between the demands of your operational schedule with those of your Circadian cycle requires intentional strategies to make sleep a priority. Here are some tips to help achieve this objective:

- On a layover, make your hotel room as cool, quiet, and dark as possible. These conditions are consistent with those during which your body is predisposed to sleep. Many find the use of sleep masks and earplugs to be helpful aids in creating the optimum sleep environment.

- Whenever possible, attempt to get as much crew rest as possible that overlaps periods when your body is accustomed to being asleep. For example, if you are normally asleep between 10 PM and 6 AM at home, to the extent you can replicate as much of this pattern as possible on a layover the quality of your sleep will be enhanced. This overlap is called anchor sleep and helps lessen the disruption to your Circadian cycle.

- Before a trip, get as much sleep as possible and monitor such things as the amount you have gotten in the twenty-four-hour periods that precede the start of a trip. Don't report for duty with sleep debt.

- Develop a consistent presleep routine that you practice both at home and on the road. These habit patterns that precede your nightly sleep period and include such things as brushing your teeth and nighttime hygiene routines. The regular and repetitive practice of these routines notifies the brain that a downshift in daily activity is underway in preparation for the intention of going to sleep. Avoid the use of electronic gadgets as part of this routine. The light emitted by smartphones, tablets, and TV screens is counterproductive to your ability to get to sleep, and to the extent your brain is being stimulated by them as you prepare to sleep, your ability to do so will be hindered.

- If you are having trouble falling asleep after about ten to fifteen minutes of lying there and staring at the ceiling, get up and walk around a bit and then go back to bed for another attempt. Consider this as a "sleep wave-off"—a trip around the pattern to set up for another approach. The worst thing you can do is lie there . . . and lie there. After a while, your inability to fall asleep will become a fixation that will increase your frustration and anxiety, both of which are not conducive to the process of falling asleep.

- Your Circadian cycle typically produces a natural and predictable dip in alertness in the midafternoon. Take advantage of this opportunity to catch a quick nap rather than stimulating your system with a triple shot of your caffeine beverage of choice. This is especially true during a layover. A midday siesta is an act of listening to your body as it expresses a desire to shut down and recharge its batteries. Don't fight a nap. Embrace it.

- Your body goes through different cycles of REM (rapid eye movement) and non-REM sleep. Non-REM sleep is necessary for physiological rest, while REM sleep is necessary for emotional and psychological refreshment. A full cycle of both REM and non-REM sleep is typically achieved in a sixty-to-ninety-minute period. For this reason, the best naps are those that are at least an hour to an hour and a half long. This doesn't mean that you forego the opportunity for a nap if this much time isn't available. Any opportunity to add to your daily quest for 8 hours of sleep is encouraged.

- Exercise regularly and eat well. Both pursuits will enhance the quality of your sleep. A healthy body fueled by nutritious food is better able to experience quality sleep than one ravaged by neglect or abuse.

- Avoid eating large quantities of food during the periods your Circadian clock has told your body's digestive system to take the night off. As a general rule, whenever possible it's a good idea to avoid eating between sunset and sunrise the following day. What you eat after dark is more likely to languish in your stomach until the digestion process cranks up the following morning, and ingestion of large amounts of food during this period increases your risk for both weight gain and gastrointestinal problems. Think of this as preventive maintenance that will enhance your overall health and the quality of your sleep.

4. Preoccupation/distraction. This SA warning light refers to a fixation on one topic to the exclusion of others and is often a by-product of ambiguity and confusion. Ambiguity and confusion are scan killers, and to the extent you become confused by the presentation of conflicting information from two reliable sources, your focus and attention can easily become one-dimensional as you attempt to reconcile the disparity. While preoccupation tends to narrow our focus on a particular issue, distraction diverts our attention from a particular task in favor of a totally different topic. This kind of focused attention on a particular object can quickly become a preoccupation that results in a loss of the big picture. Distractions occur with the introductions of new or unexpected information that redirects our attention from our primary task in favor of something that offers the promise of greater interest. Staying heads down to program the FMS while the aircraft is taxiing is an example of preoccupation, and choosing to respond to a text message notification during your initial crew briefing is an example of distraction. Preoccupation causes us to focus solely on one specific issue, and in that moment our ability to process additional information or respond to inputs from others is limited and at times nonexistent. The popularity of smart phones has made this SA warning light far too common in everyday life. We have all had the experience of seeing someone walk across a busy parking lot engrossed in their device to the point of being oblivious to the presence of moving traffic in their midst. The only thing worse than having low SA is having none. Distraction invites us to add extra and often unrelated topics into our scan pattern, and in these moments we are given to the belief that our focused attention to them is not resulting in a degradation in our overall level of operational awareness.

Preoccupation and distraction are similar in their ability to undermine our *Threat Scan*. Preoccupation tends to focus our attention on one blip to the exclusion of all others, and distraction diminishes our scan's effectiveness with the addition of extra blips to an already crowded screen.

Preoccupation is something we can bring with us in the form of an underlying personal issue like stress. Just as the forces of weight, lift, thrust, and drag influence the airframe's performance, personal stress levels can impact your performance as a crew member. With regard to the performance of the aircraft, there is a specific point on its operational envelope at a jet aircraft can achieve maximum endurance and a propeller aircraft maximum range. This point is represented by your best lift/drag ratio and is commonly referred to as L/D max. L/D max represents a point of optimized efficiency and for the purpose of this discussion consider stress to be unwanted drag that will degrade your ability to operate at your peak level of performance.

Stress represents emotional drag on our personal airframe that degrades our performance and is a type of preoccupation that drains our battery. While pilots typically excel in their ability to compartmentalize the issues that command our mental attention, it is imperative that you recognize the presence of situations that elevate your stress to levels that undermine your ability to bring your best to the flight deck. With regard to stress, it is important to understand that each of us has a stress L/D max beyond which our ability contribute to the success of the operation will be degraded. Each person's L/D max is different, and there is a wide disparity with regard to each person's tolerance for stress. One person's tidal wave can be little more than a ripple for another.

Stress Values of Life Events

What is your personal stress L/D max? That depends. Factors such as temperament, age, circumstances, and experience are some of the many variables that can determine your L/D max. Self-awareness is critical to understanding what raises your stress meter to is maximum operational limit and developing proactive measures to counter its effects on our performance. This may require a periodic inventory of the stressful events and circumstances in your life and the development of a plan to address some directly and jettison others altogether.

The following table represents the Social Readjustment Rating Scale[3] (SRSS) developed by Dr. Thomas Holmes and Dr. Richard Rahe in an effort to identify the amount of stress an individual typically experiences as a result of significant life events. In this model, stress is categorized by applying weighted life change values to specific events and assigning them a numerical score that reflects their impact on a person's life. The higher the score associated with a specific life event, the greater amount of stress the person is likely to experience.

I am not a licensed counselor, and this tool is not offered as a means of providing specific guidance for the calculation of a number that constitutes your stress limit. Rather, use it as a means to evaluate the degree to which significant events in your life are conspiring to command your time and attention to the point that your ability to compartmentalize has been exceeded along with your effectiveness as a crew member. Think of this as your L/D max scorecard, and consider the fact that the higher your overall number, the greater the likelihood you are preoccupied with matters that can adversely impact your ability to operate safely, legally, and reliably. Operating beyond your stress L/D max will cause the preoccupation SA warning light to flash.

---

[3] "Holmes, Thomas H., and Richard H. Rahe. "The Social Readjustment Rating Scale." Journal of Psychosomatic Research 11.2 (1967): 213-218.

Rank	Life Event	Mean Value	Rank	Life Event	Mean Value
1.	Death of spouse	100	23.	Son or daughter leaving home	29
2.	Divorce	73	24.	Trouble with in-laws	29
3.	Martial separation	65	25.	Outstanding personal achievement	28
4.	Jail term	63	26.	Wife begins or stops work	26
5.	Death of close family member	63	27.	Begin or end school	26
6.	Personal injury or illness	53	28.	Change in living conditions	25
7.	Marriage	50	29.	Revision of personal habits	24
8.	Fired at work	47	30.	Trouble with boss	23
9.	Martial reconciliation	45	31.	Change in work hours or conditions	20
10.	Retirement	45	32.	Change in residence	20
11.	Change in health of family member	44	33.	Change in schools	20
12.	Pregnancy	40	34.	Change in recreation	19
13.	Sex difficulties	39	35.	Change in church activities	19
14.	Gain of new family member	39	36.	Change in social activities	18
15.	Business readjustment	39	37.	Mortgage or loan less than $ 10,000	17
16.	Change in financial state	38	38.	Change in sleeping habits	16
17.	Death of close friend	37	39.	Change in number of family	
18.	Change to different line of work	36		get-togethers	15
19.	Change in number of arguments		40.	Change in eating habits	15

Remember that as with fatigue, there is limit beyond which your performance degrades to the point you are no longer an operational asset. Self-awareness and maturity are required for acknowledging when you have no business strapping into an aircraft.

Stress-induced preoccupation and fatigue are individual SA warning lights that must be monitored as a function of your *Preflight Self-Check*. A big part of your responsibility as a crew member is to present yourself fit for duty. This means you are technically, physically, and mentally prepared to operate at the levels of performance that are expected of a professional. If you can't give a thumbs-up to each of these aspects of your fitness, you are showing up for work as an unreliable instrument on the panel. Attempting to "power through" those moments when your limits have been exceeded is an exercise in poor judgment that jeopardizes the safety of the operation. Don't try to be a hero. Don't strap into an airplane in which your brain and body are not fully prepared to lead the way.

Crew SA requires the ability to cycle your attention from the general to the specific while maintaining a balanced degree of focus on both. Maintaining Crew SA requires the ability to manage your attention between specific items that require your attention while staying abreast of the bigger operational picture. A moving aircraft doesn't afford the luxury of being able to pull over and investigate a problem and to the extent you find yourself spending an inordinate amount of time and attention on a particular item chances are good that something else is being overlooked. Your scan is a dynamic practice, and the longer it is allowed to become fixed and static, the greater the likelihood that the preoccupation SA warning light will begin to flash.

> The preoccupation SA warning light flashes when your *Threat Scan* becomes a stare. Fixed attention to a single object when the aircraft is moving can threaten safety, as the aircraft doesn't stop and wait for you to catch up.

5. Rushing. The tempo of flight operations can be fast-paced, especially during the high workload phases of flight such as departure and arrival. These high-density operational arenas often require quick and accurate responses to rapidly changing situations, and the natural expectation is that we will have to "up our game" in order to keep up with the herd. Given the fact that pilots tend to be "type-A, can-do" individuals, there is often little consideration given to the possibility that they can't comply with the myriad of demands imposed during these up-tempo situations. Rather than key the mic and confess to the world that you can't hack it (better to die than look bad), the common response is simply to run faster and jump higher in an effort to meet the expectations imposed by external forces. The danger of this response is the loss of attention to precision in favor of speed as your hands race to accomplish more tasks than your brain can process. Simultaneous attention to multiple tasks increases your probability of making an error, and this likelihood increases exponentially with the introduction of a faster pace of operation. Expanding your to-do list while not allowing extra time for its completion is an invitation to error. Your attempts to do more in the same amount of time will come at the cost of precision, and important tasks are more likely to be overlooked or accomplished in a substandard manner. This is true in every aspect of life, and to the extent it defines the operational climate of your crew the rushing SA light will flash.

> Steady hands enhance flight safety. Fast hands can undermine safety when they are allowed to outrun your brain.

While I am all about doing what is reasonable in the pursuit of an on-time departure or managing speed and configuration in an effort to do my part to ensure proper flow control during the approach, neither of these objectives should come at the cost of safety. There are times when prudence and good judgment warrant a conscious decision to take your time and in these moments the most important thing to do is slow down rather than speed up. This requires an ability and a willingness to recognize when you've become task saturated to the point that your capacity for personal speed has reached its limit. In these moments it is important to resist the temptation to interpret every request from others as an automatic requirement for compliance. When it is your judgment that compliance with a request for additional speed or an accelerated descent on the arrival will put you in a position from which you will not be able to make a stabilized approach, it's not only OK but also advisable to convey your inability to comply with these instructions rather than reflexively jumping through the requested hoops. "Unable" is a more acceptable response to an unreasonable request than an automatic "can do" reaction that can undermine safety. Fly your own airplane and refuse to allow others to make decisions that are contrary to the best interests of flight safety. Slow down when you are feeling the squeeze to over-pack a five-pound bag. This pressure can come from external forces such as ATC or a published schedule, and while they should be considered and respected to the greatest extent possible, in no case should they be allowed to assume command for the safe operation of the aircraft. That buck stops with you.

Unless you are on fire or about to run out of gas, there are few instances when the operational music of the flight deck needs to be played at a tempo that makes it impossible to dance. Let someone know when you are feeling overwhelmed by the pressure to operate at a pace that exceeds your ability to accurately process what is happening. We've all been there, and your call for help will indicate the presence of a flashing SA warning light. By saying nothing, you are refusing to admit that you are in deeper water than you can manage. When you feel yourself drowning, it is better to let others know of your situation than to allow them to assume that you can swim.

In the moments on the flight deck when I felt overwhelmed by the combination of an increased tempo of operations and a greater workload imposed by the expectations of others, I found it useful to give myself verbal reminders to *"slow it down"* or *"step back for a second"* as a way of reminding myself not to take on more than I could handle. As I got older, my reflexive "can do" response to external requests and demands became more measured and I found myself more likely to respond with *"stand by"* when I began to feel overloaded.

While it was always my inclination to do what I could to enhance and contribute to the reliability of the operation, with time and experience I came to appreciate the fact that simply rushing to comply with every request often comes at the cost of safety. The link between rushing to accomplish additional tasks and the commission of unforced errors is both strong and undeniable, and this awareness taught me the value of revising the "can do" mindset to one of "can do if able." This shift blends the desire to comply with increased demands and expectations with a recognition of your capabilities and limitations. *"Can do if able."* is a slogan of discernment rooted in the memory of self-inflicted wounds that resulted from allowing yourself to operate at a pace that invited errors.

Whenever I flew with an inexperienced FO, my initial briefing would include an emphasis on the importance of pursuing safety, legality, and reliability in their proper order. This briefing would make mention of my preference for accuracy over speed, especially during the very busy and often stressful periods associated with getting the aircraft from the ramp to the departure runway and from the top of descent to the arrival gate. To the extent unforeseen circumstances like a paperwork anomaly or a weight and balance issue would invite the possibility of a delay, precision would be given preference over the pursuit of punctuality. A delay of two or three minutes is an acceptable price to pay for making sure that essential calculations are done correctly. Being on time is less important than being fully ready to go.

> When placed in a position that requires a choice between precision and an on-time departure, choose option one. Don't release the parking brake until you are fully prepared to go flying.

6. Willful Violation of SOP. At a basic level, SOP represents a form of communication in that it establishes an operational language whose syntax is clarity and certainty regarding your mutual expectations. When both members of the crew are operating in accordance with SOP, the language of safety is being spoken, and its meaning is clearly understood.

SOP establishes the framework for operational trust on the flight deck. This trust is built on the belief that the operation will be conducted in accordance with these norms and the expectation that each person is equally committed to this pursuit. This trust is violated when one person disregards the operational contract, and in that moment additional SA warning lights are likely to begin flashing as confidence is replaced with ambiguity, confusion, and poor communication. The presence of these additional warning lights will likely prompt the introduction of distraction as your brain tries to reconcile the gap between what was expected and what is happening. The choice to violate SOP is also an invitation for conflict to take a seat on the flight deck, and to the extent such behavior is chronic, resentment is sure to develop and metastasize as others are put in the position of having to communicate in a language known only to you.

> Willful violation of SOP betrays the trust of your crew and is a statement of your desire to leave the band in pursuit of a solo career. This selfish behavior undermines flight safety and voids any claim to effective leadership or professionalism.

7. Interrupted checklist or habit pattern. One of the elements of the definition of CRM is the ability of the crew to effectively manage a myriad of resources in the execution of their duties. As it turns out, there are times when simultaneous demands from multiple resources will compete for your attention. The interruption of a knock on the cockpit door as you perform the before-start checklist or a call from dispatch during your departure briefing are examples of situations in which uninvited and unwelcome visitors can conspire to derail your train of thought.

Interruptions insert themselves into our midst and demand our attention while we are engaged in other activities and, just as with rushing, the "can do" reflex often tempts us to believe that we are capable of tending to both activities simultaneously with equal degrees of precision. You'll know when you have fallen prey to this temptation when you find yourself doing something like talking to dispatch *while* reviewing the details of your departure instructions fully confident that you are capable of giving full and equal attention to both. When one task on the flight deck is interrupted by the introduction of another it is important to remember that trying to accomplish both simultaneously increases the probability of making an error. In these instances you must prioritize your attention and it's up to you to determine the order in which each task is accomplished.

> Don't take the bait of believing that you can accomplish multiple complex tasks simultaneously with no degradation in performance or SA. One conversation at a time is plenty.

Interruptions are an unavoidable part of life, and aviation is no exception. It has been my experience that interruption most often invites itself onto the flight deck during the predeparture phase of flight. The process of getting the aircraft from the gate to the runway is often an active blend of symphony and jazz as multiple teams are engaged in the common pursuit of an on-time departure. Given that each team has unique challenges and responsibilities there is the need to share information that may impact the ability to meet the stated goal. The knock on the door by maintenance or the call from dispatch typically brings the promise of new and essential information that will impact the operation and for which adjustments must be made.

Here are some key things to remember about this SA warning light.

First of all, expect to be interrupted. Never lose sight of the fact that operational success requires the coordinated efforts of a significant number of people whose responsibilities may overlap one another at certain times. Their commitment to shared goals is such that the interruptions they introduce are prompted by a desire to ensure that you are in possession of information necessary for the performance of your duties. To the extent they encounter problems that have the capacity to influence the safety, reliability, and legality of the operation you can expect to be interrupted. Think of such interruptions as the headline of a breaking news story that will directly impact your life.

When these interruptions occur, I recommend against multitasking and in favor of prioritizing. Having a conversation with dispatch about fuel calculations while completing the before-start checklist in an attempt to keep things flowing smoothly is foolish.

Have one conversation and then the other. It won't take as much time as you may think. Whenever I was interrupted by an outside source while engaged in a briefing or a checklist, it was my preference to suspend the conversation with my FO in favor of tending to the external matter. Solicitations for conversations of this type were typically time critical and in many cases included people who were looking for information that would determine their next course of action.

At the conclusion of what I considered to be the more pressing conversation, I would backtrack my conversation with the FO to make sure nothing was omitted before we moved to another topic. In the case of a checklist or briefing that was only partially completed when the interruption came I would start over from the beginning. Yes, that means that some things were checked or set for a second time, but given the choice between redundancy and the possible omission of an important item or task I considered this to be a solid trade. Don't consider such procedural overlaps as a hardship but rather as insurance against the commission of an error. The extra minutes required by these procedural overlaps are a small premium to pay for the security of knowing that nothing has been overlooked.

> Interruptions require the choice of engaging in one conversation over another. When the more pressing exchange is finished, re-engage the other with safety in mind. The extra time this will require is a worthy investment in the operation.

Let's talk for a moment about habit patterns. Habits are like well-worn footpaths of the practices and preferences created by our brains in their quest for order and simplicity. These predictable patterns of behavior satisfy the brain's desires while offering the promise of efficiency and accuracy. Habits are good and necessary as long as they don't sacrifice precision in the pursuit of simplicity. The practice of committing emergency procedures to memory and practicing them in the simulator is designed to develop and reinforce habit patterns that will serve you well in a dire situation.

Flight deck habits are the approved mental shortcuts we deem necessary for the completion of complex tasks. While interruptions certainly frustrate our established patterns of behavior, there are times when these disruptions to our normal routine can be anticipated in advance. The requirement to deice prior to departure is just such an example. This seasonal and typically infrequent occurrence requires procedures and checklists that are in addition to our normal flow and as such invite a greater need for effective coordination with others both on and off the flight deck. In the case of an event such as deicing, the disruption to normal habit patterns is one that can be known in advance and for which proactive measures can be undertaken to ensure that these additional requirements don't result in an oversight of something important. It is on such occasions that a thorough and complete briefing is especially critical. In addition to the technical and compliance aspects of the deicing procedure, there is a need to discuss the delegation of crew duties and the accomplishment of procedures that may elevate the chance of error as they prompt a deviation from your customary preflight routine.

In these instances, it may be helpful to create reminders of unfinished business. I highly recommend the use of attention-getting props and visual aids to help accomplish this goal. An empty coffee cup on the flap handle that reminds you not to configure the aircraft until certain requirements are satisfied at the conclusion of the deicing process or a sticky note on the instrument panel reminding you to monitor your holdover time are examples of simple but effective tools to help mitigate the adverse effects of having your habit pattern interrupted.

> Visible and tangible props can remind you of the need to complete specific tasks during infrequent event such as deicing. This is a safety habit worth adopting.

8. Not addressing discrepancies. This SA warning light flashes brightly when an obvious problem is not being addressed. This is the light of secrecy and it shines brightest when Solo SA is elevated to a higher priority than Crew SA. The history of aviation accidents tells a sad tale of the frequency with which crews have gone to their graves in possession of critical information known only to them that could have averted the tragic outcome. A common source of the failure to address discrepancies is the self-doubt experienced by junior crew members who are reluctant to speak up. This reluctance is usually rooted in a blend of inexperience, a desire not to risk personal embarrassment or the irritation of the captain if their concerns prove to be unfounded. When you find yourself in a situation like this, the dialogue with yourself will likely include statements such as, *"No one seems concerned, so maybe it's not a big deal,"* or *"What if I'm wrong? I'll look stupid or make the captain angry."* In any case, the remedy that seems most inviting in these moments is to say nothing and hope it all works out OK. And why not? Given the fact that things usually do work out just fine, saying nothing and playing these odds seems like a safe bet that doesn't involve the risk of conflict or embarrassment.

Rather than taking the gamble, I would recommend that you think of such situations like this: At the risk of being redundant let me again say that the fact that you are even having this conversation with yourself is a pretty good sign that you need to go public with your concern. Sometimes the questions we ask ourselves provide the guidance we need to take appropriate action. Worried about being embarrassed if your concern turns out to be much ado about nothing? Get over it. Keeping secrets because of the personality and demeanor of the captain? Get over that as well. The fear of frustrating others is no excuse for willful silence.

> Secrets serve no purpose on the flight deck. Don't hide an operational concern behind a wall of self-doubt.

9. Failure to meet or set targets. Consider targets to be short-term goals that are necessary in the planning and execution of the operation. At designated points along your route of flight you will compare your planned fuel (your target) with your actual fuel. To the extent the target fuel for a particular waypoint has been missed, adjustments to the flight plan may be required. The response to the disparity between your target fuel and actual fuel will depend on other variables but what is certain is that this will necessitate a conversation on the flight deck. Only then can Crew SA be maintained

In the case of situations that require the formulation of contingency plans think of an instance in which unexpected weather at your destination results in the requirement to enter a holding pattern. As you are making your racetrack pattern around a fixed piece of the sky, fuel becomes an issue of critical importance and this prompts the need for a discussion about the establishment of a specific time or fuel state at which you must proceed to your alternate.

In this instance, planning is incomplete unless and until it includes the establishment and acknowledgement of these targets in order to establish clear expectations for the crew. This target becomes your short-term SOP, and the SA warning light will begin to flash when such a target is not set or if it is established and later ignored at the designated point in time.

Reaching the designated target and either trying to talk yourself into one more trip around the pattern in the hope of an approach clearance or disregarding it altogether is a decision against good judgment and a violation of your agreement with the crew. When this happens the SA warning lights of confusion, ambiguity, poor communication, and a violation of SOP will begin to flash and once again the failure to address a single light will prompt the illumination of others.

Familiarize yourself with these SA warning lights and be proactive in your response to their presence. Safety is compromised when they are missed or dismissed and unforced errors are more likely to occur in either instance. Remember, if something doesn't look right or doesn't feel right chances are good that there is a flashing SA warning light in your midst.

Chapter 12

Be Decisive

Know the Principles of Sound Decision-Making

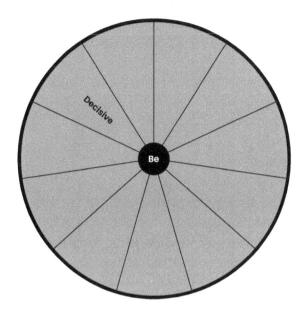

Sound decision-making is possible only when the boundaries of the Crew Envelope are respected. Operational decision-making begins with the leadership of the captain. Leadership must be exercised in a manner that enhances Crew SA through the open exchange of critical information. To the extent these disciplines are cultivated during the team formation process and reinforced during the operation, the decisions made by the captain and executed by the crew are more likely to maintain the priorities of safety, legality, and reliability.

The PIC is the ultimate authority with regard to the conduct of the operation, and as such, the decisions of the captain are binding. Operational decision-making requires the confidence to make quick and sometimes bold decisions in stressful situations. While there may be times in which you will not agree in principle with a course of action outlined by a captain, to the extent the announced decision does not violate legal guidelines or compromise flight safety, it is your responsibility to follow his or her guidance.

In this chapter we will discuss some typical methods used by people to make decisions and discuss some of the most common decision-making errors in aviation.

The two basic cognitive templates we use to make decisions are:

1. **Automatic**
2. **Executive**

1. Automatic Decision-Making. This is the method used in the majority of our daily decisions, and it is developed over time through the repetition of habits and the strength of our preferences. This means that what we like and what we have done before exert great influence in our everyday choices. The myriad of daily decisions that involve even the smallest issues such as what to order, what exit to take, or where to park become automated in the sense that such choices are essentially re-enactments of what we have done on a regular basis over an extended period of time. To the extent these decisions have produced satisfactory outcomes they are more likely to be repeated in the future.

As suggested by the word automatic, these types of decisions require minimal amounts of mental effort, and the result is a process that is generally fast and efficient. Some have theorized that humans make as many as 35,000 decisions in a given day.[4] The majority of the decisions we make on a daily basis are the individual choices whose impact is generally limited to ourselves. These choices are typically influenced by such factors as cost, convenience, time, and past experience. Given the brain's desire for order and simplicity, we are inclined to automate the decision-making process by combining our assessment of these factors

---

[4] Dr. Joel Hoomans, the Leading Edge, March 20, 2015

with past experience.

2. Executive decision-making. This method is typically utilized in making the "big-deal" decisions of life for which the potential consequences are both significant and long-term. Executive decision-making typically involves thoughtful deliberation of pertinent variables and potential outcomes and is more likely to include solicitations for advice and counsel. Executive decisions are those for which the impact is more likely to extend beyond the immediate and will involve matters such as:

- Where to live/which house to buy
- Where to go to college/which profession to pursue
- Which job to take
- Where to send your children to school

The executive method relies more on working memory and the investment of extra time and attention to gather and analyze data than its automatic cousin. Decisions made by this method are typically those for which there is limited past experience from which to develop confidence in future choices. It is for this reason that executive decision-making includes a greater degree of risk assessment than the automatic process. Another difference is that while automatic decision-making tends to be fast and efficient, the methodology used by the executive process is generally slower and more thoughtful. The executive method operates in a more sequential and deliberate manner and is used extensively in problem solving and learning new tasks. While the reliability of *automatic* decision-making tends to remain consistent over time as our habit patterns and preferences become more established, the effectiveness of the *executive* process tends to deteriorate as we age. With age comes an inability to master new technologies and complex procedures and this strengthens our reliance on what we already know. This explains why older people are reluctant or unable to adapt to new innovations in technology. Anyone who has ever helped their grandparents set up their new TV that includes more features than their old one can attest to the veracity of this fact.

> Automatic decision-making is strengthened by productive personal habits. Successful executive decision-making requires effective crew skills.

Aviation requires a combination of automatic and executive decision-making. The amount of time and attention given to personal study habits and preparation or the order in which you conduct preflight activities involve habit patterns for which the automatic process is dominant. Decisions about whether to add extra fuel or divert to your alternate are unique and complex situations for which an executive process must be employed. The habits that govern your automatic decisions will influence your executive decision-making, and for this reason it is wise to inventory the preferences and behaviors that influence your *Preflight Self-Check* on a regular basis. To the extent your automatic decisions elevate convenience and minimal effort over the pursuit of excellence, your effectiveness in the larger arena of executive decision-making will suffer. When your automatic decisions routinely prioritize expediency over excellence, your executive decision-making is more likely to value shortcuts over sound judgment. While the impact of automatic decisions is typically limited to the individual, executive decisions are those whose influence ripples out to the entire operation.

> Unhealthy shortcuts cultivated from automatic decisions can be counterproductive to the deliberative process required for executive decision-making.

In addition to the precepts of automatic and executive decision-making, any discussion of the decisions necessary for the safe, legal, and reliable conduct of the flight must also include consideration of the two arenas in which operational decisions are made. The theaters of operation that govern aviation decision-making are the *strategic* and the *tactical*, and success in both arenas requires a blend of automatic habits and executive collaboration. Let's take a closer look at each.

Strategic decisions are those made with a view toward long-term planning and possible outcomes, while *tactical* decisions are those made in real time in the course of the execution of *strategic* plans. Generally speaking, strategic decisions are based on big-picture facts and information that are analyzed while sitting still and involve an element of deferred risk and consequence. Tactical decisions are made in response to operational realities encountered while the aircraft is moving and involve increased levels of risk assessment and immediate consequences.

> *Strategic* decisions require skill at planning and analysis while *tactical* decisions require the ability to think on your feet and respond to changing or unexpected circumstances. Safety demands proficiency in both operational arenas.

Strategic decisions require the structure and predictability of a symphony, and tactical decisions often require the improv of a jazz ensemble. The decisions made during the process of flight planning require strategic thinking, while those required to deal with enroute surprises such as a systems anomaly or weather going below minimums at your destination are situations in which tactical decision-making is required. While the consequences of poor strategic decisions may not be realized until later on, the impact of tactical decision-making errors can be both immediate and disastrous, and for this reason, they are more stressful. The luxury of having time to consider the impact of a long-term strategic decision is one that is not usually available in the tactical arena.

It is in the tactical arena that we are most prone to the decision-making errors that threaten flight safety, and it is here that our CRM skills are put to their greatest test. Tactical situations have a way of reorganizing our priorities and creating a disconnect between what we know and what we believe. To underscore this point, let me use a tactical arena with which we are all familiar:

Imagine that the light turns yellow as you approach a traffic intersection, and you must make a quick decision about what to do. Should you slam on the brakes in an attempt to stop prior to the crosswalk, or will you floor it to get through the intersection before the light turns red? This is a split-second decision made with a blend of automatic pattern-matching as you assess factors such as your speed, the proximity of other vehicles, road conditions, and the presence of traffic cameras and compare them with past experience (and outcomes). Furthermore, these calculations are made in a matter of seconds without input or deliberation and once there is a commitment to a particular course of action a subsequent decision to reverse course when presented with new information becomes very difficult. It is in these tactical situations when we are most prone to influences that can reorient the order of our commitments to safety, legality, and reliability in a manner that results in poor decisions that can result in tragic consequences.

This illustration is particularly apt in that the priorities of safety, legality, and reliability that guide flight operations also govern the manner in which we operate a vehicle. The operational arenas of flying and driving share the goals of getting to our destination safely and avoiding traffic citations, and in both instances there is usually a motivation to arrive at a time that meets our expectations or those of someone else. Because of these similarities it is not a stretch to say that the tactical decision-making habits you apply in an airplane will mirror those you employ in a car.

> The *strategic* priorities of safety, legality, and reliability can quickly be reordered in *tactical* situations that require quick decisions. In these moments, the things you know to be true can be forgotten in favor of what you believe to be most important in the moment.

With regard to both flying and driving, safety and legality require compliance with the laws of physics and conformity to established rules and regulations. These guidelines are known to all involved, as are the potential consequences for violations. Reliability is a more subjective metric and is typically defined by the expectations imposed by internal or external factors such as the desire to meet a personal goal or a prescribed schedule. While safety and legality are the stated top priorities of both pilots and drivers, these two considerations can easily and quickly give way to the goal of reliability when the pressure of meeting prescribed expectations is threatened.

Your strategic self enjoys the luxury of time and the absence of immediate consequences and is given to greater certainty about the proper course of action in a hypothetical situation. The recommendations given by the strategic self are confident regarding what needs to be done and in their proclamations about the things they would "never" do in such a situation. Decisions made by your strategic self include assessments ordered by what you "know" to be true and appropriate for a situation and for which the operational hierarchy seems easy and straightforward. Your strategic self is given to confident proclamations of what you would "never" do in a specific situation and is often quick to offer judgments about the tactical decisions of others. It is in the low-risk, low-threat strategic theater that we are most confident in our ability to exercise judgment and maintain the proper operational hierarchy of safety, legality, and reliability in our operational decision-making.

By comparison, your tactical self is more influenced by stress-inducing variables of your situation as you consider the immediate risks and potential outcomes of your choices and actions. In a tactical decision the potential fallout from being late to a scheduled event can influence your risk assessment to such a degree that you can elevate reliability to the top of your list of decision-making priorities and give little regard to safety or legality. In a tactical situation, your decision-making can be influenced more by the conviction that punctuality is the most critical concern than a consideration for the risks to safety and legality that result from your decision. When this happens, what you knew to be true before you got into the car has been eclipsed by what you believe in the moment as a result of your assessment of the tactical situation.

Things always look easier when you are sitting still than when you are moving. Seeing ice accumulate on your wings during the descent to your destination invites a higher level of stress than reading the forecast during your preflight planning. Both offer different perspectives of the same reality, and the actual experience has a way of elevating your stress and skewing your judgment in a way that reading about it cannot. When your hands are on the controls of a moving aircraft and the responsibility for determining a proper course of action is on your shoulders, strategic clarity can give way to tactical uncertainty.

> Don't be too quick to make proclamations about what you would "never" do in a particular situation. It is often the case that confidence is something you have before you fully understand your circumstances.

The stress associated with tactical decision-making can persuade us to jettison what we know to be prudent with regard to the safest course of action in favor of what we believe to be most reasonable in the moment.

Tactical decisions are those for which time compression and enhanced risk exercise the most influence. In emergency situations for which there is little time and a high degree of risk associated with a decision and its consequences, it is usually the case that written procedures and the reinforced habits of training prove their worth.

In tactical situations for which there is ample time to engage in the formulation of a decision and game plan, here are some recommended steps that will enhance the likelihood of sound decisions.

1. **Ensure aircraft control**
2. **Diagnose and decide**
3. **Monitor and update**

1. Ensure aircraft control. As stated earlier, the first priority and unwritten rule of any situation are to ensure that someone is flying the aircraft. *Aviate. Navigate. Communicate.* Given the fact that pilots tend to be problem solvers by nature, the impulse to resolve the issue at hand will be a strong one that can override the top priority of ensuring that someone is minding the store.

Airborne situations that involve a systems anomaly or the requirement to analyze new information can easily result in a simultaneous dive by each member of the crew into the deep waters of problem solving. I saw this happen a number of times during my years as a sim instructor and must confess to having given in to the same impulse on occasion when I became aware that something needed fixing. It's an easy temptation, but one that must be resisted. In a complex situation that requires detailed involvement and coordination in the formulation of a plan, it is best for the FO to assume the role of PF. This frees the captain to gather essential information necessary for managing the situation. It's easier to manage the complexities of a situation when you aren't focused on flying and navigating the aircraft. Make sure the transfer of aircraft control is verified and there is no doubt about who is flying and who is working the problem.

2. Diagnose and decide. This step involves several considerations, and every effort should be made to follow them in order.

A. *Establish targets.* In an operational situation, fuel is time, and how much you have of one determines how much of the other can be spent determining a proper course of action. In such instances, it is important to establish a specific time and/ or fuel state (target) at which a plan should be executed. For example, when holding at your destination in anticipation of improved weather conditions, establish a target time and/or fuel state at which you must proceed to your alternate if the weather has not improved. Once established, this target becomes your short-term SOP unless and until new information prompts the need for a revision.

B. *Gather essential data.* This step involves a high degree of coordination, as the crew must prioritize the information deemed most critical for a decision and plan of action. This may require communication with ATC and the company as the necessary pieces for this operational puzzle are gathered. Crew SA will be enhanced when these conversations are monitored by all.

C. *Outline options.* After the information is digested by the crew, it is time for a brief and succinct summary of available options. This outline is a factual assessment of available options and should be conducted by the captain in a manner that doesn't favor a particular outcome. When the captain shows a preference for a particular option before seeking input the likelihood of receiving agreement rather than an honest recommendation is increased.

D. *Seek input and recommendations.* Having developed a shared mental model based on a clear summary of options, it is time to ask for recommendations. This step works best when this invitation is extended first to the most junior member of the crew. To the extent the FO is asked for recommendation prior to hearing a preferred course of action from the captain, he or she will be more apt to speak freely about recommendations. Asking *"what is your recommendation"* is a more effective method than saying, *"here's what I think we should do. Don't you agree?"*

E. *Announce a decision.* After critical information has been gathered and analyzed and potential options and recommendations have been summarized, it is time for the captain to announce a decision. This should be done with clarity and precision and a willingness to address questions or concerns.

F. *Brief the gameplan.* This operational huddle in which the captain is both quarterback and coach follows the announcement of the decision. It is here that the play is called and specific assignments are given to each member of the team, and this engagement is complete only when there is confirmation that everyone knows the plan and their respective roles.

3. Monitor and Update. Once a plan has been outlined, it is critical to monitor the **P**eople, **R**esources, and **E**xpectations to ensure that what is happening is consistent with what was briefed. Proactive monitoring ensures a timely response to information that may necessitate adjustments to the plan and is most effective when it is shared immediately. Information that may prompt a revision to the plan must be evaluated according to its impact on the priorities of safety, legality, and reliability. Don't fall in love with your game plan to the point that you are unwilling to revise it when the receipt of new information necessitates a change.

Risk Assessment and Decision-Making

Any decision invokes an element of risk, and this reality applies to both the strategic and tactical arenas of operation. If we allow it, experience can reduce our strategic decision-making to a rote formality and elevate expediency to a higher priority than safety. When this happens risk assessment becomes little more than a nagging mantra whose voice is drowned out by such considerations as "what we've always done" or "what works." In these instances, continued success and the absence of adverse outcomes can conspire to stifle the effectiveness of your *Threat Scan*. The elevation of past experiences and successful outcomes to positions of prominence can come at the cost of judgment and can create a type of operational momentum that reduces a *Threat Scan* to an obligatory glance. When things have gone so well for so long, your brain becomes trained to scan more for signs of assurance rather than a search for danger. When this happens, you are on the path to becoming *dangerously good,* as what you know is now subject to the template of your own experience and success.

> When your briefings become rote speeches and your active *Threat Scan* becomes a passive search for reassurance, you have become *dangerously good. Dangerously good* pilots are more prone to poor decisions. Don't allow experience to undermine safety.

To the extent that your operational priorities in a tactical situation become shuffled and no adverse consequences are realized, this realignment is more likely to occur in the future. The absence of immediate consequences from a decision to continue an unstable approach to meet the schedule rather than executing a go-around makes this behavior more likely in the future. Your confidence in what you know to be a reliable foundation for safe operation has been undermined by a situational belief and a process has been initiated in which safety becomes more of a concept than a driving operational force.

The example of the traffic intersection that illustrates the ease with which our decision-making priorities can be rearranged when the light turns yellow also applies to the approach and landing phase of flight. This represents the most dangerous intersection in aviation, for it is in this operational arena that the greatest number of decision-making errors that result in CFIT and ALA mishaps are made.

Risk Filters

It is during the approach and landing phase of flight that the temptation to abandon what we know in favor of what we believe in the moment is strongest, and it is here that we are most susceptible to the influence of *Risk Filters*. A *Risk Filter* is any belief or perception that rearranges your operational priorities and undermines your tactical judgment and decision-making. *Risk filters* breed an abandonment of what we know about the criticality of safety and legality in favor of what we believe about the immediate demands of reliability.

Here are some common *Risk Filter* that can replace focused attention on what we know with a type of "perception vertigo" that entices us to rely solely on what we believe in the moment. Perception vertigo skews risk assessment and leads to ill-advised short cuts in our decision-making.

1. **Auto brain**
2. **Absence of immediate consequences**
3. **Fascination with the goal**
4. **Follow-the-leader syndrome**

1. Auto brain. To the extent you have engaged in a particular activity over a long period of time during which you have not experienced an adverse consequence as a result of your decisions, your assessment of the risks associated with this activity slowly and predictably erodes. Like decision-making, our risk assessment can become automatic. Activities for which you once exercised caution because of the potential for adverse consequences can become routine events for which little thought is given with regard to the amount of risk involved. While this tendency to allow success to undermine our appreciation of the risks associated with an activity is common to every human activity its presence on your flight deck represents a potential threat to safety.

Think again to when you first learned to drive a car. Consider how experience and success make us less mindful of the risks associated with our driving habits over time. The same auto-brain process that makes you a *dangerously good* driver will conspire to undermine the effectiveness of your risk assessment and decision-making on the flight deck.

The dark side of experience is that long periods of uninterrupted success erode our appreciation of the risks associated with specific activities and the vigilance required to maintain an acceptable margin of safety. This happens as the result of the reinforcement of a fundamental belief shared by all of us that *"bad things only happen to other people."* This belief explains why people are shocked and surprised when they are involved in an accident or are the victim of a crime. *"I can't believe this happened to me,"* is a common response that underscores the presence of this disconnect between expectation and reality.

At a basic level, every person ascribes to this kind of idealized optimism, and pilots are no exception. While we are aware that accidents and violations do occur and have plenty of occasion during ground school and safety seminars to review case studies of accidents and incidents, these reviews often invoke a practice of distancing ourselves from embracing the possibility of finding ourselves in similar situations. It is for this reason that our prevailing attitude during presentations about the misfortunes of others is often characterized by the thought, "Yeah, I can see how they got themselves into this situation, but I would never let things get that far out of hand."

Not so fast. I have made many presentations in ground school settings that featured an in-depth analysis of airline accidents involving experienced and respected crews. The purpose of these accident reviews was never to point fingers and second-guess the actions of those involved, but to understand the chain of events that led to the tragedy and gain insight into how we may learn critical lessons that would help us avoid the same mistakes. In some instances, I would show an animated re-enactment of what the accident crew was looking at as they descended on their approach and would periodically stop the video and engage the class in a discussion of what was happening on the flight deck of the accident crew. Whenever I would ask for input regarding what should be done in this situation, I would get a significant number of answers that often combined a textbook recitation of the proper procedures that should have been executed in this instance and confident proclamations about never allowing themselves to be in a similar position. These were the responses of very experienced aviators whose careers had been free of operational misfortune. Thousands of hours of mishap-free flying had slowly cultivated a latent sense of immunity from such errors in judgment. With each additional hour of experience, this misplaced conviction skewed the effectiveness of their operational risk assessment. In their minds, years of success were a testimony to their skill and experience that offered false assurances of protection from misfortune. The inclusion of proactive risk assessment as a component of decision-making had given way to a misplaced reliance on experience and success.

Monitor yourself for these warning signs of risk indifference that can be developed and reinforced as a result of years of safe operation.

- Auto-preparation – Does *your planning and preparation for a routine flight or recurrent training involve more scanning than study and careful analysis?* If so, you are settling for assessments that are more focused on validation of that which is already known and expected over what may be discovered. Auto-prep is the mindset of one who is satisfied with "good enough" as an operational standard.

> The repetitive nature of flight operations can discourage *Proactive Flying* in favor of the expedience of auto-preparation and auto-practice. Don't let success make you complacent.

- Auto-practice—*Has the execution of your duties and responsibilities become rote and automatic?* Is your *Threat Scan* focused on alerting you to the presence of things that are out of place, or is it more given to looking for the predictable signs that offer assurance that everything is OK? Do you see and hear only what your experience has taught you to expect? A key indication of the presence of auto-ops is the frequency with which your briefings include frequent use of predictive words such as "always" and "never."

2. Absence of immediate consequences. Just as our character is shaped slowly and deliberately as a result of the small decisions we make over a long period of time, the absence of immediate adversity at the conclusion of a particular activity shapes our assessment of the risk associated with that endeavor. There are many facets in life to which this filter can apply. For example, while we have all been warned about the cause and effect links between smoking or eating foods that are high in fat content, the fact that we don't experience any immediate consequence after smoking a cigarette or eating a triple cheeseburger leads us to believe that perhaps the risks are not as real as we have been led to believe. The fact that we don't have a heart attack immediately after a cheeseburger or a cigarette gives us a false assurance that perhaps these behaviors aren't so risky after all. What we *know* from the admonitions of our doctor are eclipsed by what we *believe* as a result of our experience and in that moment our knowledge can be easily overshadowed by our belief. The application of this truth to tactical decision-making is simple and straightforward. Every pilot knows the importance of a stabilized approach and is aware of the parameters identified by their company as the basis for its definition. The time will come when you find yourself flying an approach for which your speed and configuration are outside the prescribed guidelines and will be tempted to "salvage" the approach rather than going around. To the extent you elect to continue the approach and achieve a satisfactory landing and experience no adverse consequence, you have taken the first step toward the development of a *dangerously good* philosophy of operational risk assessment. The fact that you got away with it makes it more likely that you will make a similar judgment in the future. Your salvaged approach was a triple cheeseburger and the fact that you feel fine after eating it makes it more likely that it will be on your menu in the future.

> The absence of immediate consequences to unsafe actions increases the likelihood that they will be repeated. This is the pathway to becoming dangerously good, as it erodes established boundaries of safety and objective risk assessment.

3. Fascination with the goal. There comes a point in the decision-making process when the proximity of the goal to which you have committed yourself can undermine your ability to see or consider anything else. This is a major factor in the poor decisions that often result in CFIT/ALA mishaps. A common causal factor that is often cited in these types of accidents is what accident investigators refer to as a *plan continuation error*. In short, the crew elects to continue an unstable or otherwise ill-advised approach when executing a go-around is the more prudent decision. In these instances, the attraction of completing a task to which you have committed yourself for an extended period of time is so intense that in your mind, the issue is settled and there is no need to consider other possibilities—even when presented with overwhelming evidence to support the decision to abandon the approach. On these occasions risk assessment and judgment have given way to that upon which your eyes and your brain have fixed themselves.

Fascination with the goal is a tactical hazard that awaits you on every approach. It is developed and reinforced during the phase of flight in which the operational goal to which you have devoted yourself for the past several hours is now within your grasp. In this moment, the operational inertia that has guided your pursuit of this goal is such that the prospect of not achieving it is distasteful. For this reason, the decision to discontinue the approach and go around for another attempt almost feels like failure.

As a way of combatting this decision-making trap, here are some things to consider every time you check in with approach control. Pay close attention for the presence of four factors that can reinforce your fascination with the goal to the point that the focus of your attention will become one-dimensional to the exclusion of all other considerations. These are the factors that can fuel this unhealthy fascination:

A. Runway in sight. You have visually acquired the goal whose acquisition represents the successful conclusion of the operation. Visual acquisition of a desired target makes us less interested in other options.

B. Clearance to land. When ATC gives you public permission to acquire the goal on which your attention is focused, this has the effect of making it official. That which you have sought and desired has now been formally offerred to you.

C. Statement of intentions. Keying the mic and acknowledging your clearance to land is a statement of your intention to seal the deal. Furthermore, once you have broadcast your intention to acquire the goal, a go-around becomes more difficult in that it requires both an action and a statement that contradict what you have pledged to do. For some, going around represents a public admission of not being able to "hack it" that encourages the continuation of an unstable approach.

D. The appearance of normalcy. When you observe others landing and taking off and detect no sense of urgency or concern in their radio transmissions, this can encourage the belief that things aren't really as bad as they may seem. *"If everyone else is doing it and things are working out OK for them, then it will probably be OK for me as well."* The appearance of normalcy has been cited as a factor in CFIT and ALA events over the years. In these instances, investigators concluded that the crew's decision to continue an approach in hazardous conditions such as windshear was influenced by the fact that other aircraft were landing and taking off without incident, and none of their routine radio transmissions suggested a sense of urgency or concern.

Each of these factors increases the prospect of the creation of an operational mindset that can skew our risk assessment in ways that compromise our decision-making. Be alert for the presence of these factors during the approach and landing phase of flight, and be aware that this is where you are most at risk for a plan continuation error.

> When commitment to a goal is strongest, so, too is your potential to ignore or discount critical information that may suggest the pursuit of an alternate course of action.

The proactive engagement of the PM is most critical when all of these variables are present during the approach and landing phase of a flight, as it is here that the scan of the PF has been narrowed to a concentrated focus on the specific details associated with flying the approach. As such, only the PM will have the available mental bandwidth necessary to maintain an active scan for the presence of threats to safety. This scan includes the ability to respond to new information that may prompt an alternate course of action. During the approach the PM should consider the PF to be selectively blind and deaf, as he or she will be predisposed in that moment to see and hear only that which reinforces their commitment to putting the aircraft on the runway. The safety of the operation may depend on the PM's commitment to being the eyes and ears of the crew and a willingness to intervene as necessary to end an unhealthy commitment to an outcome that may jeopardize flight safety.

4. Follow-the-leader syndrome. Documentaries about nature and animal behavior have always interested me, and it is instructive to note the similarities between human and animal behavior in group settings. I remember one episode that detailed the migration of wildebeests across the Serengeti. At one point in their trek they came to a river, and the entire herd came to a halt and stood still for an extended period of time. Their hesitation to enter the water was not due to a lack of confidence regarding the the their ability to cross, but was the result of their anxiety about the presence of crocodiles in the river. They had become aware of a significant threat to safety along their route of flight and were demonstrating a high level of Herd SA by establishing a holding pattern as they considered their next move.

The tension of indecision that accompanied their process of risk assessment was ultimately broken by the decision of a single wildebeest to take the plunge. It was never clear if this was a voluntary act or one for which there was an assist from behind, but either way, what happened next was interesting and instructive. The decision of one animal to jump in the crocodile-infested river generated excitement and activity up and down the line and one by one others began to follow suit. Mass indecision quickly gave way to collective action, and risk assessment and decision-making became a group activity for which safety was defined by the actions of others. The threat to safety had not disappeared, as the crocs were still present, but what *had* changed was the collective perception of the risk associated with jumping in the river. The fact that others were now engaging in a behavior that only moments ago had been deemed unsafe underscored the reality that their risk assessment had been re-defined by the actions of the herd.

This reminds me of the age-old question asked by every parent: *"Would you jump off a cliff just because everyone else is doing it?"* As it turns out, the simple answer is that in certain circumstances, human behavior is not much unlike that of animals. When we are in the company of a herd the answer to the question is *"yeah, maybe. Probably."*

To the extent others are engaged in an activity, we are more apt to do likewise, and to the extent the activity in question is a public one it becomes almost a certainty that in moments of indecision we are more likely to join with the herd in following the lead of the first member who shows initiative. As the momentum of the herd's actions grows, so too will the temptation to abdicate risk assessment and decision-making to them.

This phenomena applies to operations in the terminal area and it is here that our decision-making is most likely to be influenced by the actions of others. Consider the fact that airports are often the scene of "herd operations" in which multiple aircraft arrive and depart within a prescribed window of time. The hub and spoke nature of airline ops are such that the potential to be influenced by the behavior of the herd is ongoing. As you listen to conversations on the different frequencies, you develop a mental picture of what is happening with the movement of the herd around the airport and may be tempted to follow their lead, even when doing so may not be the most advisable course of action. The fact that "everyone" else is opting to land on an icy runway with a strong crosswind when a more favorable runway is available can exert a great deal of influence over your risk assessment and the operational momentum of the herd will tempt you to follow their lead. While it is good to listen to and observe the actions of the herd, don't let them make your decisions. Don't allow their judgment to eclipse your own.

> Fly your own aircraft and don't allow Crew SA to be replaced by Herd SA.

Decision-making is the ultimate goal and purpose of CRM. This critical component of the Crew Wheel is dependent on the collective strength of the other spokes. Sound decision-making results from the combined efforts of skilled crews commanded by captains whose leadership fosters the free and open communication necessary to maintain a high level of Crew SA. This is the prescription for flight operations that maintain the proper operational hierarchy of safety, legality, and reliability. To the extent these priorities are observed in their proper order, flight safety and crew effectiveness will be enhanced. Maintaining this order will be challenging at times and flight safety demands that crew members are equally invested in these goals.

Closing Thoughts

Flying is one of the most satisfying professions, and it was both a pleasure and privilege to call the flight deck my second home for more than forty years. I feel an immense and overwhelming sense of gratitude when I consider the fact that I had the opportunity to spend the better part of my adult life fulfilling my boyhood dream. As I look back, the memories that make me smile are those associated more with the men and women with whom I flew than moving the aircraft around the sky. We all began our careers as pilots and became crew members and captains along the way. The memories of figuring out what it meant to be all three and applying the lessons from each flight to the one to follow is rewarding beyond any recollection of the numbers in my logbook. The satisfaction of a career in aviation has as much to do with the camaraderie of the flight deck or ready room as with the act of maneuvering the aircraft, and with the passage of time I think less about the stick-and-rudder aspects of flying and more about the privilege of having been a member of an extended family of professionals. It is my hope that this book will be a helpful tool for your professional development, and that your memories and experiences as a pilot, crew member, and captain will be as gratifying for you as they were for me. Make it your career goal to retire with an equal number of takeoffs and landings in your logbook. Strive always to be a spokesperson for the profession and yours will be a rewarding career.

> The worst day of flying is always better than the best day at any other job.

Printed in the USA
CPSIA information can be obtained
at www.ICGtesting.com
CBHW051625251123
2031CB00004B/4